HERBERT S. ZIM, Ph.D.
Editor-in-Chief

GEORGE S. FICHTER, M.Sc.
Managing Editor

ROBERT D. BEZUCHA
Project Director

STAFF: Alice Allen, Thomas K. Brown, Ph.D.,
Dolly Debes, Eugene Z. Dodd, Ellen A. Edelen,
James A. Hathway, Howard P. Hill, Eugene S. Kostiz,
Mary H. McCallum, Beatrice P. Monroe,
Grace Neuman, Dede Pritzlaff, Jane Quinson, Ole Risom,
Donna N. Sprunt, Ph.D., Arthur Singer,
George B. Stevenson, Harriet Terwilliger, Jos. Trautwein

CONTRIBUTORS

BIRDS

Elizabeth S. Austin and
Oliver L. Austin, Jr., Ph.D.
Curator of Birds, Florida State Museum
University of Florida

DOMESTIC ANIMALS AND PETS

Merle Ferris and
Deam H. Ferris, Ph.D.
Associate Professor
College of Veterinary Medicine
University of Illinois

FLOWERS

Alexander C. Martin, Ph.D.
Formerly Senior Research-Biologist
for U.S. Fish and Wildlife Service

INSECTS

Richard M. Baranowski, Ph.D.
Assistant Entomologist
University of Florida Subtropical
Experiment Station

ROCKS AND MINERALS

Virgil G. Sleight, Ph.D.
Professor of Geology
University of Miami

MAMMALS

Donald F. Hoffmeister, Ph.D.
Professor of Zoology
University of Illinois

NATURAL COMMUNITIES

Lester Ingle, Ph.D.
Professor of Zoology
University of Illinois

NATURAL HISTORY OF MAN

Bryce Ryan, Ph.D.
Professor of Sociology and Anthropology
University of Miami

NON-FLOWERING PLANTS

Floyd S. Shuttleworth, Ph.D.
Associate Professor of Botany
University of Miami

LIFE OF THE PAST

Frank Rhodes, Ph.D.
Professor of Geology
University College,
Swansea, Wales

SHELLS AND SEASHORE LIFE

Gilbert L. Voss, Ph.D.
Associate Professor Marine Biology
Marine Laboratory,
University of Miami

FISHES

George S. Fichter, M.Sc.
Formerly Assistant Executive
Vice President
Sport Fishing Institute
Washington, D.C.

REPTILES AND AMPHIBIANS

Hobart M. Smith, Ph.D.
Professor of Zoology
University of Illinois

STARS AND PLANETS

Ivan King, Ph.D.
Associate Professor Astronomy
University of Illinois

TREES AND SHRUBS

C. Frank Brockman, M.S.F.
Professor of Forestry
University of Washington

USEFUL PLANTS

Margaret Jean Mustard, Ph.D.
Associate Professor of Botany
University of Miami

THE
GOLDEN BOOK
ENCYCLOPEDIA
OF

VOLUME 6

Fireflies to Geckos

NATURAL SCIENCE

GOLDEN PRESS NEW YORK

FIREFLIES
Photinus sp.
0.5 in.

males

larva

female

FIREFLIES or Lightningbugs are long, soft-bodied beetles (Lampyridae). They ordinarily fly only at night, hiding in vegetation during the day. The heads of most species are completely covered by a thin extension of the thorax. Females of many species are wingless and greatly resemble their larvae. Both are luminescent and are frequently referred to as "glow-worms." Their light-producing organs are located on their abdomen, sometimes on only one segment and sometimes on several. Whereas most of the energy used by an electric light bulb produces heat rather than light, the light-producing mechanism of these insects is nearly 100 per cent efficient. It is produced by a substance called luciferin that makes a yellow-green "cold light" when combined with oxygen of the air in the presence of an enzyme called luciferase. The beetles regulate the frequency of their flashes by controlling the supply of air to their photogenic organs. Each species flashes its light at a special frequency. The light serves to bring the males and females together. Firefly larvae eat other insects. Adults feed on nectar or, in some species, do not eat.

Several other groups of insects are luminescent. Among them are the Railroad Worm, which has a series of bright lights along its sides, and several large tropical click beetles (see BIOLUMINESCENCE; CLICK BEETLES).

FIREWEEDS (*Epilobium* spp.). Forest fires often destroy the work of centuries within a few hours, leaving nothing but charred ruins. The depressing sight of black, burned-over woodlands is sometimes lessened by bright patches of pink and green, almost as though new plants had sprung out of the ashes. These pioneer plants are Fireweeds.

Tall, rather weedy plants, often three or four feet high, Fireweeds are partial to cool

FIREWEED
Epilobium angustifolium

climates. They grow throughout the northern half of North America—all the way to Alaska—and are also found in other cool regions of the world. Besides coolness, Fireweeds like plenty of light and a fair amount of moisture.

How do Fireweeds get distributed to so many places so soon after a fire? The secret is in the tiny air-borne seeds. The seeds are contained in long narrow pods which dry and crack open, releasing their plume-covered contents. Long silky hairs attached to the seeds enable the wind to carry them long distances. Only a small proportion of the seeds produced find fire-cleared or bare areas in which to grow.

Fireweeds, which belong to the big evening primrose family, are so attractive that they have been grown to a limited extent under cultivation. But the plants are likely to grow too well and spread through the garden. Another name for Fireweeds is Willow Herbs, because the leaves are long and narrow like those of willows. Fireweeds have a number of close relatives. Many grow in bogs or wet lowlands of mountain regions.

Another tall weedy plant with unattractive yellow flowers also goes by the name Australian Fireweed (*Erechtites prenalthoides*). A member of the daisy family, it often appears in burned-over areas along the Pacific coast and has seeds which are carried by the wind.

FISHERS (*Martes pennanti*), one of the largest of the weasel-like mammals of North America, have been trapped for many years for their valuable fur and are now uncommon. Fishers live in northern woods and commonly climb trees in their search for small mammals, birds, and fruits. They even kill porcupines by flipping the spiny animals on their backs and attacking their undersides where their quills are not so thick. Fishers are usually less than three feet long.

Fur trappers consider the fisher to be one of the most elusive of all the fur bearers. Fishers often follow trap lines, stealing the bait without springing the trap, or feeding on animals that have been previously caught. The pelt is rare and valuable.

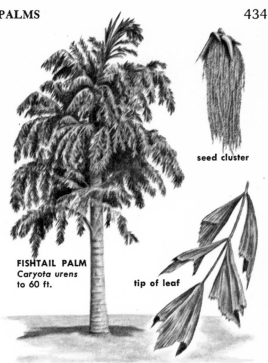

seed cluster

FISHTAIL PALM
Caryota urens
to 60 ft.

tip of leaf

FISHTAIL PALMS (*Caryota* spp.) grow in the foothills of the Himalayas, in India, and south through Malaya. They are the only palms that have leaves divided twice (bipinnate). Though not hardy, they are favorite indoor palms in large rooms where space permits them to grow naturally. The pith of fishtail palms makes an edible flour, the leaves are used for cordage, and the sap can be boiled to produce sugar.

FISHER

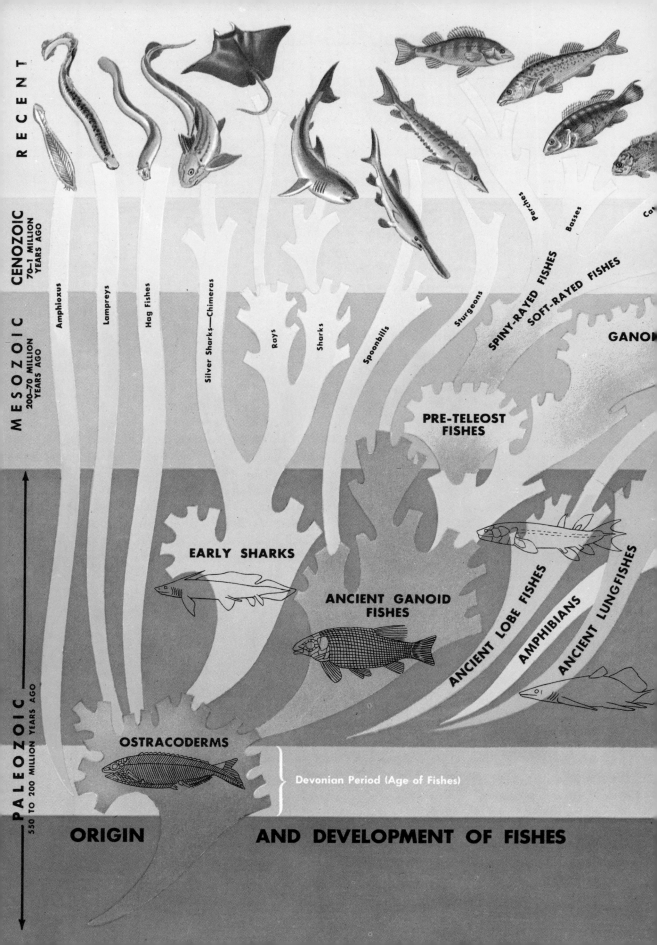

RECENT

CENOZOIC
70–1 MILLION
YEARS AGO

MESOZOIC
200–70 MILLION
YEARS AGO

PALEOZOIC
550 TO 200 MILLION YEARS AGO

Amphioxus

Lampreys

Hag Fishes

Silver Sharks—Chimeras

Rays

Sharks

Spoonbills

Sturgeons

Perches

Bosses

Cat

SPINY-RAYED FISHES

SOFT-RAYED FISHES

GANO

PRE-TELEOST
FISHES

EARLY SHARKS

ANCIENT GANOID
FISHES

ANCIENT LOBE FISHES

AMPHIBIANS

ANCIENT LUNGFISHES

OSTRACODERMS

Devonian Period (Age of Fishes)

ORIGIN   AND DEVELOPMENT OF FISHES

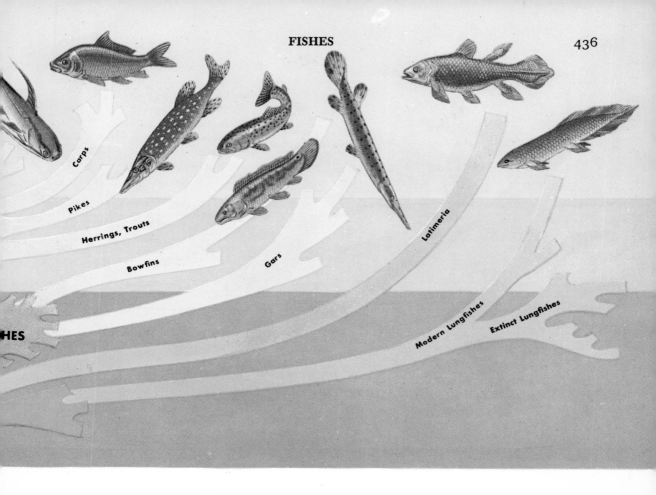

Carps
Pikes
Herrings, Trouts
Bowfins
Gars
Latimeria
Modern Lungfishes
Extinct Lungfishes
HES

FISHES are the only major group of back-boned animals completely adapted for life in the water. A fish usually has fins and scales and breathes by means of gills. And since its body temperature varies with the temperature of the water in which it lives, it is called a cold-blooded animal.

Fossil records reveal that fishes were the first backboned animals. They appeared more than 400 million years ago.

The earliest fishlike creatures, called ostracoderms, were covered with a heavy armor of horny plates and overlapping scales. In addition to their regular eyes, they had a third eye on top of their head. These primitive fishes had no jaws and only poorly developed fins. But ostracoderms did live in water—probably in fresh-water swamps—and they breathed by means of gills. They also had backbones made of cartilage, a tough tissue like that in your nose, yet not as hard as bone.

Modern fishes—and there are more than 30,000 species—developed from fishes of this sort. They are placed in three main groups. The most primitive are the lampreys and hag-fishes, direct offshoots of those ancient ostracoderms. Both are eellike and have no scales, jaws, or paired fins.

Sharks, rays, and skates, which form the second group, are not bony fishes. They have skeletons of cartilage rather than bone. This ancient group developed in the sea about 300 million years ago. They have toothlike scales and several slits opening to their gills. Bottom-dwelling sharks and rays also have a single opening, called a spiracle, on each side of their head just behind their eyes. The spiracle is used for taking in water when the fishes breathe.

Most of our present-day fishes have skeletons of bone. They make up the third group —the bony fishes. To this group belong the basses, herrings, salmons, catfishes, mackerels—the kinds of fishes most familiar to us. Most bony fishes are covered with overlapping scales. They have a single operculum, or gill

bone hook

gorge

harpoon

bone spears

50 FEET—15 TONS

Early man used spears and bone hooks for catching fish. The most primitive type hook was the gorge. A line was tied to its center, and the gorge became lodged crosswise in the fish's gullet when bait was swallowed.

cover, on each side of their head, and their fins are strengthened by bony rays.

Man's interest in fishes began far before any written records. Early man caught fishes for food. He trapped them in shallow pools and learned to catch them with his hands. Later, he made spears and nets. And finally— no one knows how long ago—he learned how to make a hook and catch fish with bait. The most ancient type of hook, called a gorge, was a straight piece of wood or bone sharpened at both ends. A line was tied to its center, and then the gorge was baited. As soon as a fish swallowed the bait, the line was pulled tight. This lodged the gorge crosswise in the fish's gullet. Some primitive peoples still use a gorge-type hook to catch fish.

Fishes are one of the most important food resources in the world. Nearly 50 billion pounds are harvested from fresh and salt waters every year. Commercial fishermen now use modern inventions, such as airplanes, depthfinders, and radar, to help them make their catches. Some fishes are eaten fresh, many are canned or frozen, and others are salted or smoked. Some kinds are processed for animal foods, to get oils for use in paints, or as sources of vitamins A and D.

Sport fishing is highly important, too. Thirty million Americans go fishing every year, for fishing is the most popular outdoor recreation. More than two billion dollars are spent annually in the United States by sport fishermen for tackle, boats, and fishing trips.

Other people enjoy keeping fishes as pets in aquariums. Or they visit the large public aquariums where fishes of many kinds and sizes are displayed. Scientists, in their studies of fishes, have learned much about living things in general as well as about the adaptations of fishes to their watery world. Fishes are, indeed, one of the most important, most interesting groups of animals.

INTERNAL ANATOMY—A typical bony fish, the Striped Bass, is used here to illustrate the fish's simple digestive system, the position of the two-chambered heart, air bladder, kidney, and other internal structures. Note the broad, W-shaped muscles.

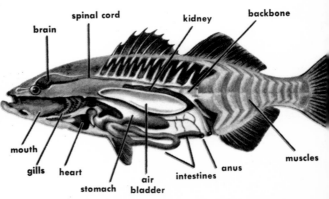

brain
spinal cord
kidney
backbone
mouth
gills
heart
stomach
air bladder
intestines
anus
muscles

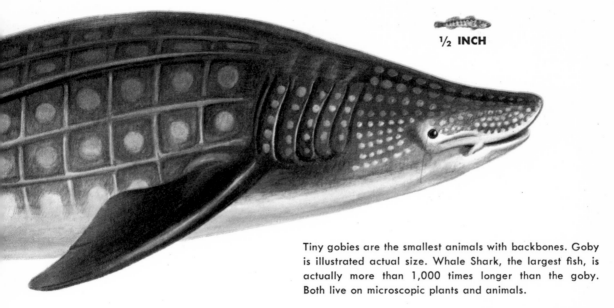

½ INCH

Tiny gobies are the smallest animals with backbones. Goby is illustrated actual size. Whale Shark, the largest fish, is actually more than 1,000 times longer than the goby. Both live on microscopic plants and animals.

SIZES

Tiny gobies that live in fresh-water lakes in the Philippine Islands are the smallest fishes in the world. They are, in fact, the smallest backboned animals, for even when full grown, they still measure less than half an inch long. Men catch these little fish in fine-meshed nets and sell them in the markets to be baked into fish cakes. It takes nearly 15,000 of these gobies to weigh a pound!

At the opposite extreme are monstrous Whale Sharks that roam the warm oceans. These giants may measure as much as 50 feet in length and weigh more than 15 tons. Whale Sharks, despite their size, are not dangerous. They feed mainly on plankton, the very small plants and animals that float in the sea. (See PLANKTON.)

In fresh water, sturgeons rank as the largest fish. Russia reports catches of sturgeons that weigh as much as a ton and a half. Sturgeons that weighed more than 1,000 pounds were once caught in the Snake River in western United States, where a sturgeon half that size is rare now. (See STURGEON.)

EXTERNAL ANATOMY—Pectoral and ventral fins are paired—one fin on each side, like our arms and legs. Dorsal, caudal, and anal fins, located on the midline of the body, are not paired. Most fishes are covered with scales and have a visible lateral line.

Next in size among fresh-water fishes are giant catfish. The Wels, found in the Danube and other rivers of Europe, tips the scales at 400 pounds or more. The Pla Bük, a catfish that lives in Siam, weighs more than 500 pounds. Many kinds of fresh-water fishes exceed a hundred pounds in weight. Alligator Gars of the lower Mississippi and its tributaries may weigh more than 300 pounds. Paddlefish, also found in the Mississippi drainage, may weigh several hundred pounds. (See CATFISH; GARS; PADDLEFISH.)

But most giant fishes live in the sea. Of these, one of the most unusual is the Ocean Sunfish, or *Mola mola*. Known to weigh as much as a ton, this strange fish appears to be all head, for its fins are set far back on its broad, almost tail-less body. Basking Sharks reach a weight of five tons. Mantas may also

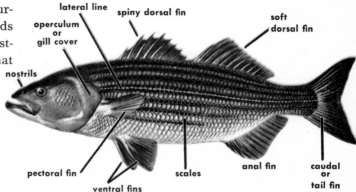

lateral line · spiny dorsal fin · soft dorsal fin · operculum or gill cover · nostrils · pectoral fin · ventral fins · scales · anal fin · caudal or tail fin

weigh a ton or more. There are several species of sharks, tunas, and marlins that may attain a weight of more than a thousand pounds. (See MARLINS; OCEAN SUNFISH; RAYS; SHARKS; TUNAS.)

Record fish are sought by all fishermen and rival claims can cause arguments. To qualify his catch for an official record, a fisherman must provide complete details, such as the kind of tackle he used, where he made his catch, and the fish's weight on tested scales. This is to make certain that the official records contain no "fish stories."

Often, of course, there is a great difference between the largest fish caught on rod and reel and the size to which that kind of fish is known to grow. For example, the largest Tarpon ever taken on hook and line weighed 283 pounds. But a Tarpon that weighed more than 350 pounds was netted by commercial fishermen off the southeast coast of Florida a few years ago. It just happens that no sport fisherman has yet been lucky enough to catch one this large.

Most of the Brook Trout caught by anglers weigh less than half a pound. Yet the record catch is 14 pounds 8 ounces. Still another, the record Largemouth Bass weighed 22 pounds 4 ounces, but the average size caught is three pounds or less.

If food is plentiful, a fish grows rapidly at first. Its growth slows down after it becomes mature, but the fish continues to increase in size slightly every year as long as it lives. In warm waters fish grow more rapidly than in cold waters, largely because there are more months in the year in which they can feed. For this reason a three-year-old bass in southern United States may weigh more than a bass twice as old from a northern lake or stream. Bass from Florida's many inland waters are notably larger than bass from any other area of the United States and therefore are classified as a subspecies.

RECORD FISH CAUGHT ON ROD AND REEL

SALT WATER

FISH	WEIGHT	FISH	WEIGHT
Albacore	69 lbs.	Pollock	40 lbs.
Amberjack	120 lbs. 8 oz.	Roosterfish	100 lbs.
Barracuda	103 lbs. 4 oz.	Sailfish, Atlantic	123 lbs.
Bass, Channel	83 lbs.	Sailfish, Pacific	221 lbs.
Bass, Giant Sea	551 lbs.	Sawfish	754 lbs.
Bass, Striped	73 lbs.	Shark, Mako	1,000 lbs.
Blackfish or Tautog	21 lbs. 6 oz.	Shark, White	2,664 lbs.
Bonefish	18 lbs. 2 oz.	Shark, Thresher	922 lbs.
Bonito, Oceanic	39 lbs. 15 oz.	Shark, Tiger	1,422 lbs.
Cobia	102 lbs.	Snook	50 lbs. 8 oz.
Cod	72 lbs.	Swordfish	1,182 lbs.
Dolphin	76 lbs.	Tarpon	283 lbs.
Drum, Black	94 lbs. 4 oz.	Tuna, Yellowfin	266 lbs. 8 oz.
Flounder, Summer	20 lbs. 7 oz.	Tuna, Blackfin	44 lbs. 8 oz.
Kingfish	77 lbs.	Tuna, Bluefin	977 lbs.
Marlin, Blue	780 lbs.	Wahoo	136 lbs.
Marlin, Black	1,560 lbs.	Weakfish	17 lbs. 8 oz.
Marlin, White	161 lbs.	Weakfish, Spotted	15 lbs. 3 oz.
Permit	42 lbs. 4 oz.	Yellowtail	105 lbs. 12½ oz.

FRESH WATER

FISH	WEIGHT	FISH	WEIGHT
Bass, Largemouth	22 lbs. 4 oz.	Perch, Yellow	4 lbs. 3½ oz.
Bass, Smallmouth	11 lbs. 15 oz.	Pickerel, Chain	9 lbs. 3 oz.
Bluegill	4 lbs. 12 oz.	Pike, Northern	46 lbs. 2 oz.
Bullhead, Black	8 lbs.	Salmon, Atlantic	79 lbs. 2 oz.
Carp	55 lbs. 5 oz.	Salmon, Chinook	83 lbs.
Catfish, Blue	94 lbs. 8 oz.	Salmon, Landlocked	22 lbs. 8 oz.
Catfish, Channel	55 lbs.	Salmon, Silver	31 lbs.
Charr, Arctic	17 lbs. 12 oz.	Trout, Brook	14 lbs. 8 oz.
Crappie, Black	5 lbs.	Trout, Brown	39 lbs. 8 oz.
Gar, Alligator	279 lbs.	Trout, Cutthroat	41 lbs.
Gar, Longnose	50 lbs. 5 oz.	Trout, Dolly Varden	32 lbs.
Grayling, Arctic	4 lbs.	Trout, Lake	63 lbs. 2 oz.
Muskellunge	69 lbs. 15 oz.	Trout, Rainbow	37 lbs.
Perch, White	4 lbs. 12 oz.	Walleye	22 lbs. 4 oz.

Atlantic Mackerel — Spindle

Longear Sunfish — Compressed

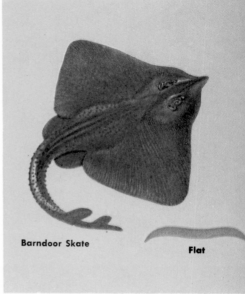

Barndoor Skate — Flat

SHAPES

A fish's shape is sometimes a clue to the place and the way it lives. Those with spindle-shaped bodies, such as mackerels and trouts, are generally fast swimmers. Fishes with this shape are found in open seas or in swift-flowing streams. Flat-bodied fishes, like flounders and rays, live close to the bottom, while fishes of quiet waters as a rule have bodies flattened from side to side so that the fish is many times taller than wide. Examples are fresh-water sunfishes and salt-water angel-fishes. These three are the most common body shapes, but there are many others that fit fishes for special ways of life.

Some kinds of fishes, such as eels and cutlass fishes, have long, snake-like bodies. A fish with this shape can slither about among water plants or into rock crevices where it hunts for its food. Others, like puffers and porcupine fishes, are globular in shape, and trunkfishes have triangular-shaped bodies, flat on the underside.

Fishes with odd-shaped bodies are generally poor swimmers. To make up for this lack, they have special protective features. Porcupine fishes can inflate their bodies to several times normal size so that their spines stand out formidably to protect them from enemies. Trunkfishes are safe inside their shell-like outer coverings.

Deep-sea fishes have the weirdest shapes in the fish world. Many have long thread-like fins at the ends of which are lights that glow in the black waters. (See ABYSSAL ANIMALS; BIOLUMINESCENCE; DEEP-SEA FISHES.)

Porcupine Fish

Globular Shape

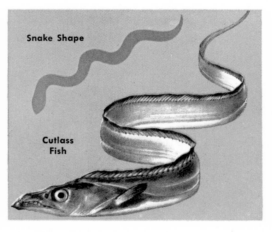

Snake Shape

Cutlass Fish

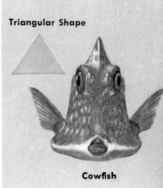

Triangular Shape

Cowfish

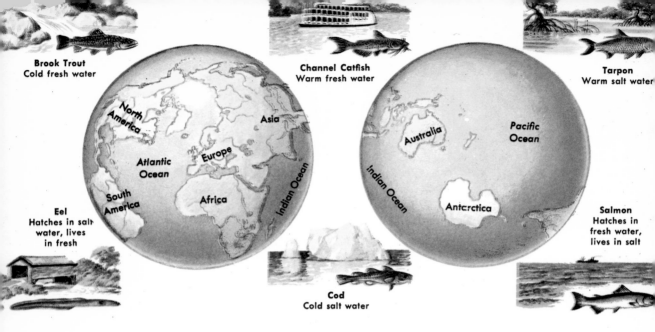

Brook Trout
Cold fresh water

Channel Catfish
Warm fresh water

Tarpon
Warm salt water

Eel
Hatches in salt water, lives in fresh

Salmon
Hatches in fresh water, lives in salt

Cod
Cold salt water

WHERE FISHES LIVE

Salt waters cover about 71 percent of the earth's surface. In addition, there are numerous lakes and streams on land areas. Despite this abundance of water, each kind of fish is in some way best suited for life in a certain type of water and even to a particular area.

Some kinds of fishes can live only in salt water; others only in fresh. Some do equally well in either fresh or salt water, while fewer still divide their time between the two.

Some fishes spend their lives swimming close to the surface in the blue waters of the open sea. Others are found only in dark waters two miles or more deep. But the greatest variety is found in shallow, tropical seas. As many as a thousand species may live in only a few square miles of coral sea, while an area the same size in a cold, northern sea may harbor no more than a dozen kinds.

In contrast, the number of individuals of one kind of fish in cold seas may be astonishingly large. Billions of herrings are harvested annually from schools so tremendous that the catch does not appear to affect their numbers.

Tropical seas contain the most kinds of fishes. Cold seas, however, are richer in individuals of a species. This is due primarily to seasonal upwellings of water that mix into the sea the rich nutrients spread over the bottom. As the sun warms the water and light reaches depths darkened during the long winter months, the sea "blooms" with plankton—tiny plants and animals that are the basic food of all fishes. Those few kinds of fishes that are adapted to life in cold waters have little competition for this abundance of food, and so they feed in these vast pastures of the sea and become fat and plentiful (see PLANKTON).

In fresh water, too, some kinds of fishes can live only in cold, swift streams, while others are confined to warm, sluggish rivers or stagnant pools. As in the sea, the greatest number of species is found in warm waters, but the schools of a single kind of fish are generally larger in cold waters.

Some kinds of fishes live in strange places. There are fresh-water fishes that thrive in hot springs where the temperature of the water is seldom less than 100 degrees Fahrenheit. Others, blind and colorless, live in the total darkness of cave waters. Blind gobies of the Pacific hide beneath rocks, clinging to them as tightly as snails. A little South American catfish lives in the gill chambers of larger fishes, chews on their gills and feeds on the blood that oozes out. There is a fish that lives in the hollow inner chamber of the sea cucumber and another that spends its life darting about in the midst of the dangerous tentacles of the Portuguese man-of-war. A colorful tropical fish of the West Indies makes its home inside the shell of a living conch.

Some fishes bury themselves in the sand or mud to hide from enemies or to lie in wait for prey. Some burrow in head first, others tail first. Flat-bodied fishes wiggle back and forth until the sand and mud stirred up settles over them. There is a minnow that literally "swims" through soft mud, almost as easily and as rapidly as other fishes move through water.

There are fishes that are found only in the raging torrents of mountain streams. Some, slim and pencil-like, creep about in the holes and crevices beneath rocks. Others have adhesive discs on their bellies, and still others hold onto rocks with sucking mouths.

Seahorses are unusual sights when out of their natural surroundings but are really hard to see among the waving, feathery seaweeds where they normally live. Sargassum fishes are virtually invisible in the floating masses of brown sargassum weeds where they make their homes.

Males of one kind of deep-sea angler fish are dwarfs compared to their mates. Early in their lives they fasten themselves to a female's body and then grow attached there. The tissues of the two fishes fuse, and the male degenerates. For the rest of his life, the male is a parasite on the female, which may eventually weigh a thousand times more than her parasitic mate.

Remoras have sucking discs on top of their head. With these they fasten themselves to sharks, turtles, or other creatures. Ancient

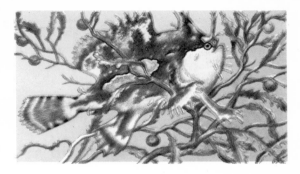

Its mottled brown color and fringed fins camouflage the Sargassum Fish in the floating seaweed.

myths credit remoras with the ability to hold back ships at sea; hence, one of their common names is Ship-holder.

Some fishes die almost immediately if they are taken out of the water. Others, such as the lungfishes, live out of water for many months in protective cocoons. Eels travel overland, crawling through wet grass. Gobies and blennies skip along the rocks from one tidal pool to another. The Climbing Perch, a strange fish found in Asia, prowls for hours among roots and over mud flats in search of food. Even when the Climbing Perch is in the water it must come to the surface from time to time to gulp air in order to survive.

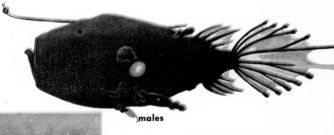

males

Four male Ceratioid Anglerfish have fastened themselves to this female and will be parasites for the rest of their lives.

Remoras have a powerful suction disc formed from their first dorsal fin. They ride through the sea attached to sharks and other creatures.

The Climbing Perch spends many hours out of the water, hanging to roots or prowling along mud flats in search of food.

HOW FISHES SWIM

Long, eellike fishes swim by wiggling their bodies like a snake does when it crawls rapidly. Their bodies make a series of flowing "S" shapes as they move through the water.

Other fishes use only their fins for swimming. Rays, for example, flap their broad and winglike pectoral fins and literally "fly" through the water. They are among the most graceful creatures in the sea. Trunkfishes, their bodies immovable in their shell-like outer covering, also swim—and awkwardly—by using only their fins.

Almost all fishes at times employ jet propulsion to give them a fast start. They do this by expelling the water forcefully from their gills. This shoots them forward. Flatfishes often use this method for making a fast getaway. They seem to explode from the bottom, and by the time the debris stirred up by their departure has settled, they are out of sight.

Ordinarily, of course, you think of one of the sleek and streamlined fast ocean swimmers when you think of a fish. Coated with slime to help reduce the friction, its torpedo-shaped body can slip through the water with little resistance. This is the shape imitated by designers of boats, airplanes, and automobiles in trying to achieve greater speeds.

These fishes get their driving power from the mass of W-shaped muscles that extend from their gill covers to their tails. These muscles are the part of the fish that we eat. They are the familiar flakes or chunks that separate from each other easily after a fish is fried or baked.

The typical fish swims by moving its whole body from side to side. This is actually the same kind of movement used by long-bodied, eel-like fishes. But fishes with short bodies make incomplete "S" shapes that cannot be distinguished easily. These fishes use their fins only as brakes or for steering. Their fins also help them to "stand still" in the water, for the water forced from their gills as they breathe tends to push them forward.

Among the fastest fishes in the sea are the mackerels, tunas, sailfishes, and marlins. Many of these swift swimmers can fold their dorsal fins into grooves on their backs so that even the slight resistance of these thin and knifelike fins is eliminated when they are traveling at top speed.

Many fishes jump to escape being caught by some other fish that is chasing them or to hurdle barriers in their paths. Others, such as mullets, apparently jump for the sheer joy of it. Many kinds jump when hooked. These make the most thrilling catches.

Some fishes make their jumps by surging up from deep water. Others swim close to the surface, then suddenly turn their noses skyward and give a powerful thrust with their tails to get speed enough to take to the air. Sailfishes can leap more than 10 feet. Flying-fishes are reported to glide as far as a quarter of a mile along the surface of the sea.

Once it was believed that a fish's tail fin was essential to its swimming. Tails do vary greatly in size and shape, and many fishes get a great amount of driving force from their tails. But experiments have demonstrated that a fish can swim even after its tail fin is cut off. In fact, if all of its fins are cut off a fish can continue to swim, though steering and keeping itself upright are difficult.

Sharks, which have poor control of their fins, can swim swiftly in a straight line, but

Flatfishes jet-propel themselves from bottom by squirting water through the gill opening on their underside.

Fishes swim fast by wagging their bodies rapidly from side to side. Long, slim fishes, such as the eel at right, also swim in this manner. Their wiggling bodies make "S" shapes as a snake's does.

neither floats nor sinks but remains suspended at whatever level it desires. All of its energy can be used for swimming. Flatfishes, such as flounders, have no air bladders, and so they do sink directly to the bottom. Sharks also have no air bladders. They have a tendency to sink, too, but the abundance of oil in their livers makes it easier for them to float.

A hooked Atlantic Sailfish thrills game fishermen by leaping high and "tail-walking" across the surface.

Four-winged Flyingfish skims along the surface of the sea, sometimes for distances of a quarter of a mile before plunging into the water again.

Rays flap their broad pectoral fins like wings and appear to fly through the water.

they have trouble in stopping or turning, as do bony fishes with large, heavy pectoral fins.

Many fishes have unusual ways of swimming, too. Seahorses, for example, swim in a "standing up" position. They get their swimming power from the wavelike motion of their dorsal fins. An African catfish swims upside down. Needlefishes and halfbeaks skitter across the surface with the front halves of their bodies held high out of the water and their tails still submerged, wagging rapidly. Other members of the same family swim with their heads down and their tails up.

A fish's remarkable air bladder, which sometimes serves as a lung and sometimes as a sound amplifier, also assists the fish in swimming. By varying the amount of gas contained in its air bladder, a fish can adjust its body weight to equal the weight of water its body has displaced. The effect of this is to make the fish have almost no weight at all; it

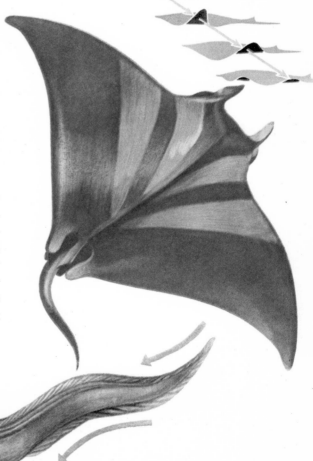

HOW FISHES BREATHE

Fishes breathe oxygen, like other living creatures. They use the small amount of oxygen dissolved in the water, absorbing it into their blood through their gills.

Watch a fish in an aquarium. It opens and shuts its mouth constantly as though drinking in gulps of water. Each time the fish opens its mouth, water flows into its mouth cavity. The gill covers, located on each side of its head just behind its eyes, remain closed while its mouth is open. Some fishes increase the amount of water they can take in by lowering the floor of their mouth cavities. Others puff out their cheeks. Still others depend on their swimming to cause water to flow over their gills, and such fish will die if they do not continue swimming.

The circulation of water through a fish's mouth and out its gill openings is easily observed by putting a drop of food coloring into the water just in front of the fish's mouth. The colored water disappears as it is drawn into the fish's mouth. A moment later it is forced out through the gill openings.

When the fish is resting, it gulps water slowly. But if it begins to swim or if it becomes excited, it opens and shuts its mouth

more rapidly. Then the fish is using oxygen at a faster rate and needs to get more of it. The fish is "breathing hard."

Each gulp of water passes over the fish's gills. These are much divided, thin-walled filaments where blood vessels lie close to the surface. The gills of a living fish are bright red, because of the numerous blood vessels.

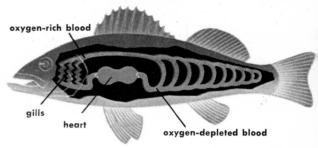

A fish's heart has only two chambers. Blood carrying oxygen from gills, which serve the same function as lungs of higher animals, moves through body at a lower pressure (less rapidly) than with more efficient four-chambered heart of warm-blooded animals.

In these gills an exchange of gases takes place. This is part of the process called respiration. Carbon dioxide, the waste material released by the cells of the fish's body and carried by the blood, is given off by the gills. At the same time, the dissolved oxygen in the water is absorbed into the blood and is transported to the fish's body cells. A fish's gills expose so great a surface area and are so efficient that as much as 75 per cent of the oxygen contained in the water is removed during the brief time the gills are bathed in each gulp of water. By comparison, we withdraw less than 5 per cent of the oxygen available to us in each breath of air.

Different fish need different amounts of oxygen, and this often determines the sort of water in which they live.

Fish opens mouth and takes in water. Gill cover is closed.

Fish closes mouth and opens gill cover. This forces water over gills.

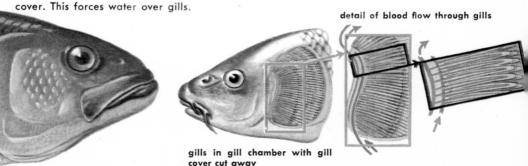

detail of blood flow through gills

gills in gill chamber with gill cover cut away

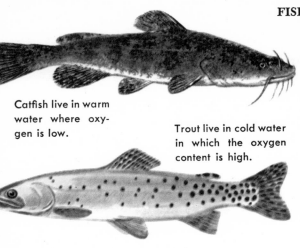

Catfish live in warm water where oxygen is low.

Trout live in cold water in which the oxygen content is high.

Trout, for example, need large amounts of oxygen. They live in cold waters, which can hold a greater amount of dissolved oxygen than do warm waters. Many also live in cool, fast-flowing waters where new supplies of oxygen are churned in continually.

Near the opposite extreme are many of the catfishes. They need much less oxygen for their survival, and so they can live in sluggish, warm waters in streams or lakes where the oxygen content is low. A catfish can stay alive for many hours completely out of the water. Carp also have low oxygen needs. Kept cool and moist, they are sometimes shipped alive to markets a thousand or more miles from where they were caught.

In the sea, oxygen is more abundant in cold, polar waters than in warm, tropical seas. And there is more oxygen near the surface where wave action stirs up the sea than in deep water or where the sea is calm.

Decaying plants remove oxygen from fresh water. Growing plants give off oxygen. On a sunny day, more oxygen is available in the afternoon after the plants have been active for several hours than early in the morning or at night. These factors may influence where fishes are found in ponds and sometimes explain why fishes move from one spot to another in any body of water.

A few kinds of fishes can breathe air just as land animals do. The most familiar of these are the lungfishes, which live in the tropics of Africa, South America, and Australia. Their "lungs" are their air bladders, which are richly supplied with blood vessels and are connected directly to their mouths.

When a lungfish needs oxygen, it comes to the surface and gulps in a new supply, taking it directly from the air. A lungfish will actually drown if it stays under the water.

In dry seasons, the stagnant pools where lungfishes live dry up. Then these unusual fishes burrow deep into the mud at the bottom and secrete a slimy, protective coating over their bodies. A small air hole connects to the surface through the mud casing over them, and through this they continue to breathe air. When the rains come again and the pools fill with water, the lungfishes wriggle out of their strange cocoons.

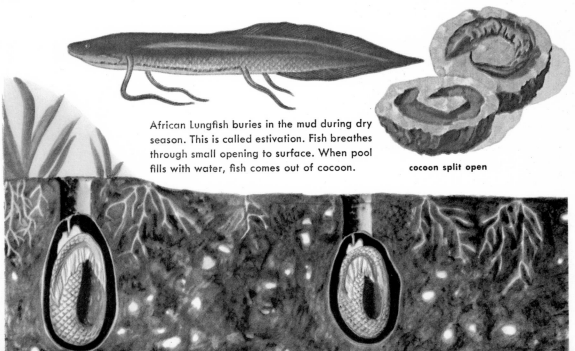

African Lungfish buries in the mud during dry season. This is called estivation. Fish breathes through small opening to surface. When pool fills with water, fish comes out of cocoon.

cocoon split open

Ganoid Scales are hard and fit close against each other. Gars and sturgeons are primitive fishes which have scales of this type.

ganoid scale

ctenoid scale

Ctenoid Scales have spiny projections on rear margin. Scales of this type are found on sunfishes, perch, and other spiny-rayed fishes.

cycloid scale

Cycloid Scales are smooth on rear surface. They are found on soft-rayed fishes, such as salmons, minnows, and pikes.

SCALES

A typical fish's body is covered by a protective coat of scales which usually overlap each other like the shingles on a roof. On the outside of these scales there is a thin, tight-fitting membrane containing glands that secrete slime. The slime helps to reduce the friction of the fish's body as it moves through the water. It is also a barrier to disease organisms that might attack the fish. This slime makes a fish slippery and hard to hold.

The total number of scales on a fish's body remains the same throughout its life. New scales are added, however, to replace any that are lost, and each scale increases in size as the fish grows larger. Periods of rapid growth or lack of growth are recorded on the scales as ridges and spaces. These are like the annual rings in the trunk of a tree.

Biologists learn much about a fish's past history by studying its scales. For one thing, they can determine its age, since the seasons of abundant food and fast growth are easily distinguished from the periods of food shortage and slow growth. These usually correspond to summer and winter, a pair of rings equaling one year's growth. Between these most prominent lines there are smaller lines that reveal other events in the fish's life. An expert fish scale reader can tell at what age the fish spawned for the first time, how often it has migrated, whether it has been sick, and which years have been its best. The age of

placoid scale

Placoid Scales of sharks and rays are covered with a hard outer coating of enamel. Sharkskin with these tooth-like scales still attached is called shagreen.

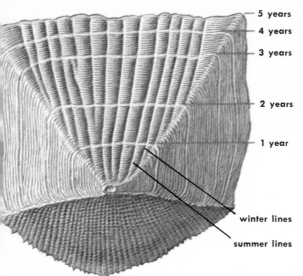

During winter, fish grow very slowly, and so "growth rings" on scales are close together. They are almost a solid line. In summer, fish grow rapidly, and rings are far apart. By counting the number of winter rings, we can determine the fish's age.

fishes that do not have scales can be determined by counting similar growth rings in certain bones, but to do this, the fish must be killed. Scales can be removed from a fish without harming it seriously.

Counting rows of scales and the number of scales in rows on the fish's body is also a method used to tell one species from another. Often two young fish of the same size will look much alike, but a scale count will reveal that they are different species. Common White Suckers, for example, have 80 or fewer scales in the lateral line row. Sturgeon Suckers look like the Common White Sucker, but have more than 85 scales.

Fishes do not have scales when they first hatch from the egg, but their scales begin to grow within a few weeks. Most catfishes never grow scales. They remain "naked" or smooth-skinned throughout their lives, protected by their slippery skins, which are often tough and leathery, and by the sharp spines in their fins. Paddlefish have no scales. Sculpins have only a few which are greatly modified. Mackerels have very tiny scales. Swordfish have scales when they are young, then lose them as their "bills" develop. Trout have tiny scales that are covered by their thick

skin. Eels, too, have widely separated scales that are buried deep in their skin. In contrast, a Tarpon's large silvery scales may measure several inches across.

Fish scales are of several different types. Most bony fishes have the familiar thin, shingle-like scales. Some of these have stiff spines along their rear margins. Other scales have smooth rear margins.

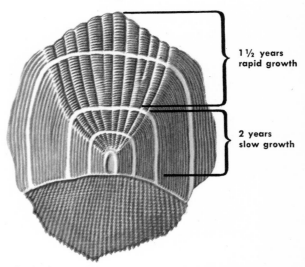

Scale from a 3½-year-old salmon shows how salmon grew slowly during its two years spent in fresh water, then grew much more rapidly in the sea.

Garfishes, primitive modern fishes, are covered with hard, almost bony scales. Those of a sturgeon are enlarged and shell-like so that they form ridges of armor along the sturgeon's back and sides.

Sharks have still another type of scale. They are enamel-coated and have a dentine core, similar in structure to our teeth. Shark-skin with these small, hard scales still attached is called shagreen. It was once used to make non-slipping covers on knife and sword handles and as a kind of sandpaper.

Shark's spiny scale resembles a tooth in structure. Each scale is covered with enamel and has a pulp cavity. The shark's teeth are similar.

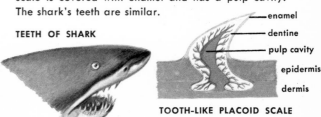

TEETH OF SHARK

TOOTH-LIKE PLACOID SCALE

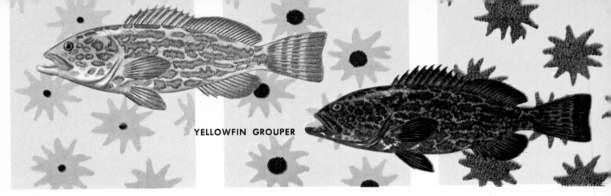

YELLOWFIN GROUPER

With the pigment pulled to the center of its star-shaped chromatophores (left), this Yellowfin Grouper is a light color. To the right, the pigment has spread throughout the cell so that the fish is dark.

COLORS

The familiar silvery color of a fish's scales is due to a deposit of guanine, a by-product of protein digestion. In some fishes this deposit is heavy and almost chalky white. In others the crystals act as prisms, breaking up the light that strikes them and producing metallic, iridescent hues. The pigment colors —the blacks, greens, yellows, reds, and their various combinations—are caused by special cells, called chromatophores. These numerous star-shaped cells are scattered throughout the fish's skin.

By varying the amount of pigment in these cells many kinds of fishes can change their colors to suit their moods or to match their surroundings. The pigment in a chromatophore cell can shrink until only a small spot is visible. At other times the pigment expands and fills the whole cell.

Sometimes these color changes take place rapidly. They can occur as a fish swims from one type of background to another. Or a fish

A flounder matches its background by varying the size of the white and dark patches on its body. A blinded flounder can no longer make these changes.

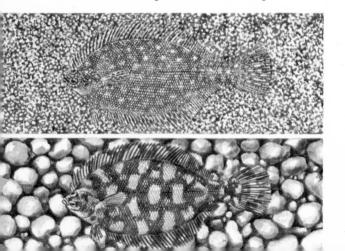

may flush with color at the sight of an enemy as some male tropical fishes do when they see another male. Often the colors seem to ripple as they change from one color to another. This may happen when a fish has just been caught and is brought into the boat. This sort of color change is commonly observed in Dolphins and is caused apparently by fright or shock. (See DOLPHINS.)

When a fish is angry, its color generally becomes darker. When it is frightened, its colors become paler, and it is also more pale than usual when it is ill.

Color changes are generally brought about by sight, for a blinded fish is unable to make color changes to match its environment. This is demonstrated by flounders. Blinded, a flounder remains the same color no matter on what background it is placed. Normally, however, a flounder is able to match its surroundings with remarkable accuracy. Over a sand bottom it becomes a yellowish-brown color. But the instant it moves over a dark-colored bottom, its color changes to almost black. And, most remarkable, if the flounder swims over an area mottled with dark and light it becomes spotted, too. Experiments have shown that flounders can almost achieve the square-checked pattern of a checkerboard. Nor are the flounders restricted to black, brown, and white. Some can become reddish, yellow, or green.

Normally a flounder is white on its underside. All of its pigment cells are located on the top surface. But a flounder put in a glass-bottomed aquarium with lights shining through from below soon acquires pigmentation on its belly side, too.

SENSES

Most fishes are nearsighted. Since light does not penetrate far in water, distance vision would be of little use to the ordinary fish. But at close ranges a fish can see clearly, especially moving objects.

The lens in the human eye is slightly curved. It is equipped with special muscles which can change its shape so that the eye can be focused on objects that are close or far away. But the lens in a fish's eye is almost spherical, and since its shape cannot be changed, its focus is pre-set for seeing near objects. Some fishes do have muscles attached to the lens so that it can be moved back and forth slightly to get a sharper focus.

Light rays travel at a greater speed in air than in water, which is more dense. Therefore the rays are bent as they pass at an angle from the one medium to the other. A man must remember this when shooting a fish with a bow and arrow or when casting a lure directly to a fish, for the fish is really closer than it appears to be. The light rays are not bent as they travel from the water to a point directly overhead, so from straight above the fish is located exactly where it appears to be.

Also because of the bending of the light rays, the fish looks from water at objects in air through a sort of circular window. The circle's outer edge is formed where light rays strike the surface at an angle great enough so that they are bent back into the water again. Objects just within the fish's range of vision appear around the edge of this window, while those directly overhead appear in its center.

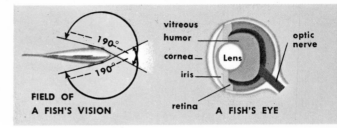

Fish's eyes on sides of head give it good vision toward rear and at sides and a small area (shaded white) of binocular vision straight ahead.

One of the oddities in the fish world is the Four-eyed Fish, which lives in the shallow water of muddy streams in Central America. Its bulbous eyes, located on top of its head like a frog's, are always half in the water and half out of the water. It really has only two eyes, but they function as four because of their internal structure.

The lens in the Four-eyed Fish's eye is egg-shaped rather than spherical. When the fish looks under the surface of the water, light rays pass through the entire length of this lens. The Four-eyed Fish's vision in water is as

Fish looks through a circular "window" on the surface of the water since light rays that strike surface are bent back (dotted line) into the water again when they strike surface at great enough angle. Everywhere beyond the point of refraction the surface appears opaque.

Fish appears to be along dotted red line due to bending of light rays as they pass at an angle from water to less dense air. Light rays traveling directly to bird overhead are not bent.

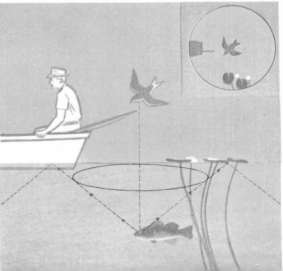

Archer Fish are accurate marksmen at distances up to four feet.

nearsighted as any other fish's. But when it looks out into the air, light passes through the shorter width of the lens. This gives the fish good distance vision in the air.

Most fishes have no eyelids. Their eyes are constantly bathed in water, and so they have no need for eyelids to keep their eyes moist, which is the principal function of our eyelids.

Some sharks, however, have three eyelids. In addition to upper and lower lids, they also have semi-transparent membranes which move across their eyes. These lids work independently of the upper and lower lids. They slide over the shark's eyes to protect them from sand, mud, or other debris stirred up as it feeds on the bottom.

Experiments have demonstrated that fishes are able to recognize colors. Black bass, for example, quickly learn to distinguish the

Barbels, or whiskers, around a fish's mouth are used as tasters or feelers in finding food.

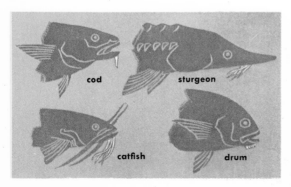

color red when it is associated with food. Then, in order, they learn green, blue, and yellow. There is a good possibility that some fishes may prefer one color to another or that water conditions will at times make one color more easily recognized than at others.

Archer Fish are outstanding examples of fish that have excellent vision. They actually shoot their prey by hitting them with drops of water squirted forcefully from their mouth. At distances up to four feet, they are deadly accurate and can knock spiders from their webs, hovering insects from the air, or frogs from their perches on the bank. As the Archer Fish prepares to shoot, it moves back and forth to make certain of its range.

The eyes of fishes that live in the dark depths of the ocean are frequently greatly reduced in size. Fishes that inhabit the dusky regions of the sea, in contrast, generally have enlarged eyes so that they can utilize even the small amount of light that is available. Some of these fishes have, by comparative size, larger eyes than any other backboned animals. And fishes that live in the perpetual darkness of cave waters either have very small eyes or no eyes at all.

Since it has no eyelids, a fish cannot shut its eyes when it goes to sleep, and many fishes do sleep—or rest—at regular intervals. Schools of perch, for example, scatter every night, and the fish drop down to the bottom individually to rest. At daylight they assemble in schools again. Other fishes lie on their sides when they sleep. Some "stand up" or lean against rocks or crawl into crevices. One eccentric fish dives into the soft bottom head first when it wants to take a nap. A tropical parrotfish secretes a mucous blanket around itself at night, often spending an hour or more every evening preparing its "bed."

Fishes that have poor vision may make up for this lack by having a better developed sense of taste or smell. Bullheads, for example, have taste buds distributed over their whole bodies. If a morsel of food is held near a bullhead's tail, it immediately begins opening and shutting its mouth, for it has tasted the food through its tail and is ready to eat.

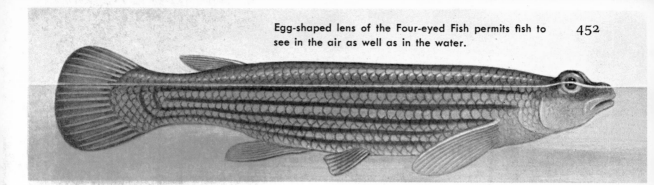

Sharks also depend on their good sense of smell to locate their food and will sometimes follow traces of an odor for long distances through the sea to its source.

The nerve endings for the sense of smell are located in the fish's nostrils. These are blind openings at the end of the fish's nose and are not used at all for breathing. Exceptions are the stargazers, which spend much of their time buried in the sand or mud. Their mouths cannot be used to channel water over their gills. Instead, they use their nostrils.

Most fishes are also able to hear sounds and can detect vibrations in the water. They learn to come to a particular spot to be fed when certain sounds are repeated day after day at feeding time. Thus, the ringing of a bell, the playing of the same music, or the sound of a man's voice may soon become associated with food. Yet a fish has no external ears or ear openings. It does have, internally, small ear bones, and since sound waves travel better in water than in air, a fish can hear noises even though it has no external ear to help capture the vibrations.

In some fishes these delicate ear bones are connected to the air bladder which serves as a chamber to amplify vibrations. Also, the fish's lateral line contains sensory cells which open to the outside through pores. Through its lateral line the fish can determine the direction of currents of water, detect the presence of nearby objects through variation in water pressure, and also sense vibrations. This ability is useful to a fish in navigating at night or in murky waters, in keeping schooling fish together, and also in finding food or escaping enemies.

Finally, some fishes are far from being quiet creatures. They can make rasping, grunting, squeaking, or squealing noises. Some make noises by rubbing together special bone extensions of the vertebrae. Other noises are made by vibrating muscles that are connected to the air bladders which amplify the vibrations. Still other fishes grind their teeth, their mouth cavities serving as the sound box to amplify the noise. Sound-detecting devices lowered into the sea to pick up engine noises of submarines or other ships during World War II were frequently "jammed" by the noises of schools of fish. Many fishes, notably croakers and grunts, make noises when they are caught.

Lateral lines, distinctively shaped and of various lengths, are important sensory organs.

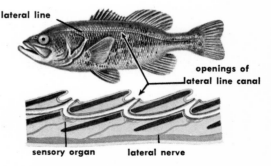

lateral line

openings of lateral line canal

sensory organ   lateral nerve

LONGITUDINAL SECTION OF LATERAL LINE

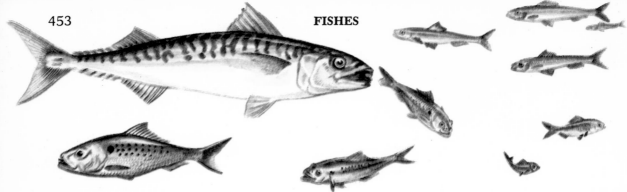

WHAT FISHES EAT

Most fishes are flesh eaters. They feed on smaller fishes or other aquatic animals. These, in turn, feed on still smaller creatures. Finally, the smallest plants and animals, those consisting of only a single cell, become food, too. These tiny plants and animals are the first step in the food chain.

These small plants and animals which float about in the water are called plankton. When conditions are right, billions of them—several tons to the acre—may be found in a body of water. Sometimes they "bloom" so abundantly that they color the sea for hundreds of square miles. Similar blooms in small fresh-water lakes or ponds may use up all the oxygen and kill the fish.

These tiny bits of life, invisible to the naked eye, are the basic food of all fishes. The illustration at the bottom of this page shows a simple food chain in the sea. Plankton is eaten by small crustaceans; these are eaten by successively larger fish. In the illustration, the plankton indirectly adds to the meal of a tuna and arrives at our table. Biologists estimate that it probably takes as much as five tons of plankton to be converted finally to one pound of tuna (see PLANKTON).

Some large fishes feed directly on these small plants and animals. Paddlefishes detect swarms of these tiny creatures with their sensitive snouts. Herrings strain them from the sea through bony sieves in their gills. Suckers and other bottom feeders sift them from the bottom oozes. Even giant Whale Sharks and Basking Sharks feed on plankton.

A fish that feeds on plants generally has a long, coiled intestine—perhaps ten times the length of the fish itself. Plant food is more difficult to digest than meat and requires longer processing. A flesh-eating fish has a short digestive tract, often shorter than the total length of the fish's body.

Fish-eating fishes generally have mouths that fairly bristle with teeth. Many even have teeth on their tongues. Yet a fish does not chew its food as we do. It swallows its food

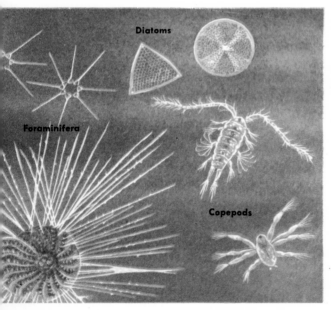

The plankton at left is magnified many times, for most of these tiny plants and animals are microscopic in size. As a basic food of fishes and other aquatic animals, they are the most important life in any body of water.

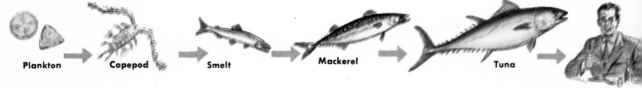

Plankton → Copepod → Smelt → Mackerel → Tuna →

whole, using its teeth only to grab and to hold the food or to tear off chunks.

Some plant-eating fishes have "teeth" in their throats. These grinders are connected to the bony arches over their gills and are used to mash up the plants before they pass on into the fish's stomach.

Catfishes, which eat both living and dead foods, have numerous small teeth, and their strong jaws get a vise-like grip on anything that comes between them. Most fishes have medium sized teeth which are large enough to catch and hold fish smaller than themselves. Northern Pike and Muskellunges, however, are real "tigers" of fresh waters. They have big mouths and numerous large, pointed teeth. These fishes will attack prey of any size. In salt water, sharks and barracudas are among the best equipped to attack prey their own size or larger.

The Eagle Ray is also called Clam Cracker, because it has flat, powerful teeth with which it crushes the shells of oysters, clams, and other mollusks to get at the animals inside.

The teeth of tropical parrotfishes are fused into sharp, powerful beaks, like a parrot's, used to bite off chunks of living coral. Butterfly fishes, pipefishes, and trumpet fishes have long, tubular snouts which can be poked into coral crannies to suck out food. Swordfish and other "billed" fishes have no teeth. Parasitic Sea Lampreys have rasping, sucking mouths with which they bore holes in other fishes and suck out their body fluids.

Several kinds of fishes, such as the Torpedo Ray and the stargazers, have organs which can produce electricity to shock and stun prey. The shocks may also frighten attackers away and, incidentally, may also be useful to the fish by detecting the direction of currents of water, thus helping it to navigate at night or in murky waters.

Nearly every body of water contains a few kinds of fishes that eat only plants, a larger number that eat only fishes or other aquatic animals, and a few kinds that are scavengers. An exception is the deep sea, where almost all fishes are carnivorous (see ABYSSAL ANIMALS; DEEP-SEA FISHES).

A sucker's mouth points down and is used to suck in bottom oozes.

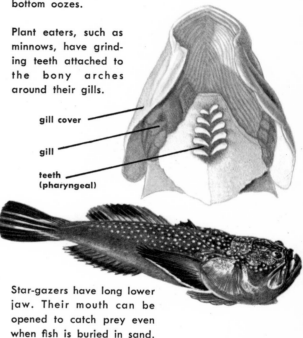

Plant eaters, such as minnows, have grinding teeth attached to the bony arches around their gills.

gill cover

gill

teeth (pharyngeal)

Star-gazers have long lower jaw. Their mouth can be opened to catch prey even when fish is buried in sand.

Barracuda's mouth is filled with long, sharp teeth, equipping this fish to hold prey of any size.

Barbels on sturgeon's snout drag along bottom. When it detects a morsel of food, the sturgeon sticks out its tube-like mouth and sucks it in.

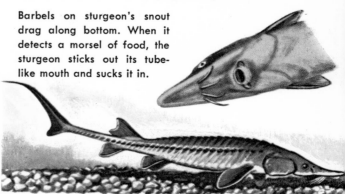

SPAWNING

Many kinds of fishes build nests in which they lay their eggs. Bluegills are examples, and as is common in the world of fishes, the male is responsible for building the nest and caring for the young.

Bluegills like company, so a group of males generally select the same area in which to nest. Each finds a spot that suits him and then starts fanning the area with his fins. As he works, he turns his body first in one direction and then another, and after much wriggling and sweeping, he has swept a saucer-shaped depression of silt and loose debris.

As soon as the nest is finished, a female Bluegill comes to lay her eggs. Average-sized females lay about 5,000 eggs; large ones may deposit as many as 50,000, often visiting several nests during a season. The male discharges milt (sperm) over the eggs immediately after they are laid.

Each egg that unites with a sperm is fertilized and begins to grow, the tiny embryo receiving its nourishment from the egg's yolk.

Only the male stays at the nest. Frequently he fans the eggs, which prevents sand or silt from settling over them. His sweeping also stirs the water surrounding the eggs. And if any inquisitive creatures come too close to the nest, the male chases them away.

In about a week, the exact time depending on the temperature of the water and other factors, the eggs hatch and the nest becomes a swarming mass of tiny Bluegills. The male continues to stand guard for several more days until the young finally venture to swim away. Then the male leaves, too.

Brook Trout also build nests, but like other trouts, they do not guard their eggs. The female is the nest builder. In a gravel area of stream rapids, she begins stirring and sweeping to make a depression in the bottom. The bottom material dislodged by her fins and body washes away in the swift current.

After the hole is several inches deep, the female lays her eggs there, and her mate fertilizes them. Then the female swims upstream just beyond the edge of the nest and begins dislodging more rocks and pebbles. These wash into the hole until it is filled. The trout continue to work their way upstream, making more nests as they go. After several weeks or months, the eggs left in the nests hatch. The young trout, with yolk sacs still in evidence, squirm out of the loose gravel.

Bluegill Sunfish

BLUEGILL SPAWNING

Male   testes

Female   ovary   sperm

sperm

egg

ova, or eggs   egg fertilized by uniting with sperm.

Male fans saucer-shaped nest . . . then squirts milt over eggs as they are laid . . . and guards until they hatch.

Not all fishes build nests, of course, but some kinds give their eggs and young really unusual treatment. Sea Catfish males, for example, carry the eggs in their mouths which serve as brood pouches. Even after the eggs have hatched, the males continue to carry the young fish in their mouths. As they grow larger, the young catfish spend more and more time outside, but if they are frightened, they dart inside to hide. Finally, when they are about two inches long, they leave the male and do not return. Then, for the first time since he began incubating the eggs, the male can eat a meal.

Common Bullheads and many kinds of tropical fishes dig burrows in which they lay their eggs. A female South American catfish carries her eggs attached to a spongy, adhesive disc on her belly. Sticklebacks make neat nests of sticks and debris, much like a bird's nest, and the males will defend them with their lives.

Male Gourami fish blow bubbles which rise to the surface and form a floating raft, the bubbles stuck together with a mucus secreted by the fish. Then the female lays her eggs beneath the nest, and her mate picks them up and blows them up into bubbles where they float about until they hatch. The watchful male stays underneath the raft and chases away any intruders. Siamese Fighting Fish also deposit their eggs in bubble rafts.

Some fishes hide their eggs in shells or beneath rocks or sticks, and others attach them to the bottom. Yellow Perch lay long strings of eggs which they stretch about in the underwater vegetation. Male seahorses carry their eggs and young in belly pouches, like opossums or kangaroos.

Fishes that build nests and protect their eggs and young do not lay as many eggs as do those that give their eggs and young no attention at all. A female Carp may lay several million eggs during a spawning season. Many of these eggs never hatch because they become covered with silt or debris or are eaten by other fishes or aquatic creatures. But enough hatch to assure there being an abundance of Carp.

Trout bury their eggs in loose gravel. When eggs hatch, the young trout squirm through the pebbles and swim along the bottom.

Codfish and mackerels also lay millions of eggs, discharging them into the open sea. Female sturgeons often carry more than a million eggs at a time, the weight of the eggs being as much as 25 per cent of the fish's total weight. Sturgeon eggs, salted and processed, are highly prized as caviar.

Still other fishes give birth to living young. The females carry the eggs inside their bodies until they have hatched, and then the young are born. Some sharks nourish their developing young by an attachment of blood vessels similar to the placenta ordinarily believed to be peculiar to mammals.

The male sea catfish uses its mouth as a brood pouch for the female's eggs. After the eggs hatch, the male continues to carry the young for several weeks.

egg   newly hatched larva

first swims upright—
eye on each side

soon turns on one side—
both eyes on upper surface

ADULT FLOUNDER

Fishes that give birth to their young produce the fewest number. Exceptions are the salt-water rockfishes. A female rockfish may give birth to as many as 30,000 young at a time. Less than an inch long when born, these tiny fish are at first nearly transparent, and they float about in the sea carried along by the currents. Several weeks pass before young rockfish acquire color and begin to look at all like their parents.

Typically, a newly hatched fish, called a larva, still carries with it an undigested supply of yolk from the egg. Its paunchy stomach makes it look much like a tadpole, but this built-in food supply gives it a day or two to adjust to the outside world before it must begin hunting food for itself.

How long it takes for a young fish to mature varies greatly with the species and also with the temperature of the water and the amount of food available. Before they transform into the parasitic adult stage, larvae of the Sea Lamprey live for as long as five years as burrowers in the soft mud on the bottom of fresh-water streams. Baby Bluegills, in contrast, begin to look like their parents within a few weeks after they emerge from the egg.

Under natural conditions few fishes ever die a natural death. As soon as age weakens them, they become food for other fishes or for some fish-eating bird, reptile, or mammal. It is known, however, that some kinds of fishes live past the age of 50 years. There are reliable records for eels and for the Wels, a giant European catfish. In the United States a Carp that lived more than 60 years was reported.

Young flatfishes make one of the most unusual transformations as they become adults. A young flatfish begins life by swimming in an upright position like any other fish. Its eyes are located one on each side of its head. Within a few days, however, the little fish begins to lean to one side. Some kinds of flatfishes always lean to the left, others always to the right. The eye on the side toward which the fish is leaning begins to move toward the opposite side of the fish's head. Within a few weeks the flatfish is lying completely on its side, and its eye has completed its migration to a position close to the other eye.

The life stories of fishes from the time the adults spawn until the eggs hatch and the young fish are mature are filled with examples of adaptations which aid survival.

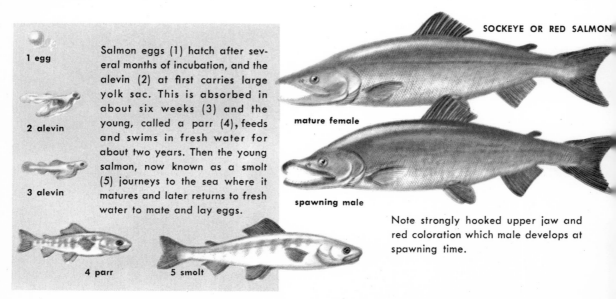

1 egg

2 alevin

3 alevin

4 parr   5 smolt

Salmon eggs (1) hatch after several months of incubation, and the alevin (2) at first carries large yolk sac. This is absorbed in about six weeks (3) and the young, called a parr (4), feeds and swims in fresh water for about two years. Then the young salmon, now known as a smolt (5) journeys to the sea where it matures and later returns to fresh water to mate and lay eggs.

SOCKEYE OR RED SALMON

mature female

spawning male

Note strongly hooked upper jaw and red coloration which male develops at spawning time.

DAILY AND SEASONAL MOVES

A bass fisherman knows that, in summer, he can catch bass in a lake or a pond early in the morning or late in the evening when the bass are feeding in the shallows. But during the heat of the day, the bass stay in the cool, deep water far from shore.

Biologists use this same principle when they want to reduce the number of pan fish, such as Bluegills, in an overpopulated pond. They put poison in the shallow water when the midday sun is hottest. Many small pan fish are killed, but most of the bass are spared because they are in deeper water.

Fishes do move from place to place to find food or to make themselves more comfortable. Some kinds never travel far from where they were hatched, while others journey thousands of miles to find food or to lay their eggs.

King Salmon, for example, may swim more than two thousand miles from the ocean to the headwaters of mountain streams to lay their eggs. As soon as they have spawned, they die, too exhausted to make the return trip to the sea.

Shad, sturgeons, and smelts also travel from salt water to fresh water to spawn. American and European eels reverse the trip, however. They journey from fresh water to salt water to lay their eggs.

For many centuries people had no idea where eels spawned. All sorts of tales were told about how eels came into being. One belief was that they came from horsehairs that fell into the water. Finally a Danish naturalist worked out the true story.

American and European Eels both spawn in nearly the same area of the Atlantic Ocean, at the edge of the Sargasso Sea. There each female lays millions of eggs, which the males fertilize. It is believed that both adults then die in the sea.

Newly hatched eels are thin, transparent, and leaf-like. Young eels, or glass fish, do not at first resemble their parents. Soon they begin drifting with the ocean currents toward fresh water.

Curiously, young American Eels travel toward North America, while the European Eels swim toward Europe—yet neither has ever seen its "home" before, and they have no guides to show them the way. For American Eels this is a trip of about 1,000 miles; for European Eels, 3,000 miles or more. It takes nearly three years for the baby European Eels to make their journey, but American Eels get home in about a year. Astonishingly, the growth rates of the two species are so different that the young of each have developed to about the same size when they reach their "home" waters.

By this time the young eels have thicker bodies and have begun to look very much like adults. At this stage they are called "elvers."

Males stay at the mouths of rivers and in coastal waters. Females continue to swim upstream. Occasionally they crawl out of the water and slither through the wet grass to get from one stream to another or to a lake or a pond. Eventually they settle down in a body of water where they feed and grow. Females may grow to a length of three feet or more in their fresh-water homes. Males rarely get to be more than a third as long.

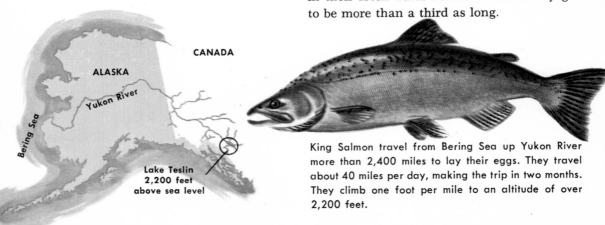

King Salmon travel from Bering Sea up Yukon River more than 2,400 miles to lay their eggs. They travel about 40 miles per day, making the trip in two months. They climb one foot per mile to an altitude of over 2,200 feet.

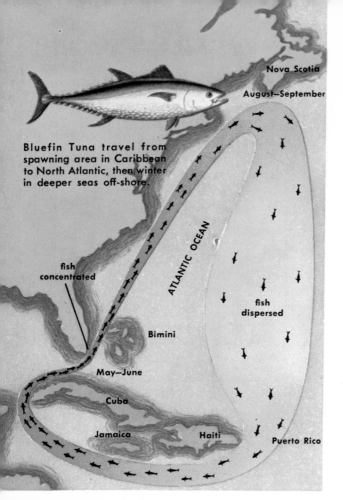

Bluefin Tuna travel from spawning area in Caribbean to North Atlantic, then winter in deeper seas off-shore.

Nova Scotia
August–September

ATLANTIC OCEAN

fish concentrated

Bimini

fish dispersed

May–June

Cuba

Jamaica   Haiti   Puerto Rico

After several years, eels lose their greenish-yellow color. They fade until almost white and are then known as Silver Eels. At this stage they are ready to begin their trip to the sea to lay their eggs. (See EELS.)

Along the Atlantic coast of the United States, Bluefin Tunas move northward every spring following the Gulf Stream. Sport fishermen meet these schools all along the route.

May is Bluefin Tuna fishing time in the Bahama Islands. Few tunas caught this early in the season weigh more than 400 pounds. By August the tunas have reached Nova Scotia, and by this time a great many of them weigh a thousand pounds or more. All during the trip they have fattened themselves on food fishes, such as Menhaden and Herring.

Dolphins, jacks, barracudas, and many other kinds of salt-water fishes drift northward in summer as the water becomes warmer. They move south again as soon as winter sets in. Other fishes, such as the Cod, come in-

shore to feed in winter but return to cold, deep waters in summer.

Fresh-water fishermen sometimes lower thermometers into lakes or ponds to get the temperature of the water at various levels. Then they fish at the depth where the water temperature is best for the kind of fish they want to catch.

Many fresh-water fishes, such as suckers and trouts, swim far upstream to build their nests and lay their eggs. Here their eggs can hatch and their young develop where their enemies are fewest.

Most extraordinary are the spawning runs of the Grunion, a small salt-water fish that lives in the coastal waters off southern California. Grunion spawn about every two weeks from March through June. They ride in on the waves of the highest tides during the full moon, just as the tide begins to ebb. Millions of silvery fishes swarm over the beaches. Females, their abdomens swollen with ripe eggs, squirm into the wet sand. In pockets several inches deep they lay their eggs, and the males quickly fertilize them. By the time the next high wave breaks over the beach, the fish have finished their spawning. They wiggle into the fast-receding waters and disappear into the blackness of the sea.

Their egg laying requires little more than a minute. Yet the timing is so precise that the eggs are deposited only on the very peak wave of this highest tide.

For nearly two weeks the Grunions' eggs develop beneath the warm sands, but they do not hatch until they are bathed once again in salt water. Then the tiny fish squirm up through the soaked sand and swim out to sea with the tide. (See GRUNION.)

Grunion spawning on the sand at peak of tide.

Richard A. Boolootian

GREATER FLAMINGO—45–50 in.
Phoenicopterus ruber
West Indies, South America, Eurasia, Africa

FLAMINGOS are colorful birds that are most abundant in the tropics of Europe, Asia, Africa, and America. They nest in shallow ponds, building a mound of mud on which to lay their one or rarely two eggs. All the eggs of a colony hatch at about the same time. Males help in incubating the eggs.

Flamingos, despite their appearance, are distantly related to geese and make the same honking sounds. Newly hatched flamingo chicks are downy white with short legs, and look like baby geese until their legs grow.

Flamingos feed with their heads and bills upside down. The birds move forward, dragging the upper bill in the silt, while the tongue creates a suction that draws the marine organisms on which the bird feeds into the bill. The lower bill is held still, while the upper bill, which is joined to the skull by a flexible plate, moves slightly.

The American Flamingo, a form of the Greater Flamingo, ranges from the Bahamas to South America and the Galapagos Islands. The American Flamingo was once an irregular winter visitor to southern Florida. By 1930 it occurred rarely and today the birds known in Florida are bred in captivity.

The Greater and Lesser flamingos breed in southern Eurasia. James' Flamingo is very rare and its breeding habits are unknown. The Andean Flamingo lives in brackish lakes in the high Andes of South America and is the largest member of the family.

In addition to the North American group, the Greater Flamingo is found in the southern half of South America and in Europe, Africa, and Asia. The Lesser Flamingo occurs only in Africa, in the great Rift Valley. Both the Andean Flamingo and James' Flamingo live in lakes high in the Andes.

FLAPFOOTED GLASS LIZARDS (about 20 species of *Pygopus, Lialis,* and *Aprasia*) are found only in New Guinea, Australia, and Tasmania. Their snakelike bodies range in length from 6 inches to 2½ feet. They lack front legs entirely, and their hind legs are short and flaplike. Some flapfooted lizards are burrowers; others live on the surface of the ground. Like American glass lizards (see GLASS LIZARDS), they can break their long tail to escape enemies. All except a few of the burrowing species have ear openings, but like snakes, they lack movable eyelids. A large transparent scale covers each eye. The vertical pupil of the eye indicates activity largely at night, like the geckos to which they are related (see GECKOS). All lay eggs and are insect-eaters.

Flapfooted skinks (*Dibamus spp.*) are blind, earless burrowers of a family related to true skinks (see SKINKS). Females lack both front and hind legs; males have flaplike hind legs, probably used in courtship. Three species (6 to 9 in.) occur from southern Indo-China to the Philippines and New Guinea.

FLATFISHES look like typical fish when they first hatch from the egg. Soon, however, they begin to lean to one side. The eye on the underside begins to migrate to the top surface, and the "blind" side loses its pigment and becomes pale or white. In some species, even the mouth twists upward. Before many weeks have passed, the flatfish has completed this remarkable transformation which fits it for a one-sided existence (see page 457).

More than 500 species make up this important group of ocean fishes, distributed throughout the world. Some species come close to shore or move into bays in summer, then return to deep water in winter. A great many kinds are valued as food fish, and millions of pounds are harvested annually. Some are caught for sport.

Most flatfishes are small and live in shallow to moderately deep waters. There they lie close to the bottom, darting up occasionally to grab fish, crustaceans, worms, or other creatures on which they feed. Female flatfish

STARRY FLOUNDER
Platichthys stellatus
15–20 lbs.

AMERICAN PLAICE
Hippoglossoides platessoides
Average 7 lbs. Up to 14 lbs.

SMOOTH FLOUNDER
Liopsetta putnami
About 1½ lbs.

SOUTHERN FLOUNDER
Paralichthys lethostigma
About 1½ lbs.

lay numerous eggs (one halibut may contain two million eggs, for example) which float until they hatch.

Soles are the smallest of the flatfishes, few of them measuring as much as 10 inches in length. Their eyes are small and close set, and their mouths greatly twisted. Filet of sole originated with a sole common in European waters; in the United States, filet of sole is made from flounders. Soles of many species are speared and netted in waters throughout the world. Few species are found in United States waters. One is the Hogchoker (*Trinectes maculatus*).

At the opposite extreme in size and habits are the halibuts (*Hippoglossus spp.*). They catch their food by pursuing small fish through the open sea. They are swift swimmers and spend less time lying in wait for prey to come by.

Halibut are sometimes netted by commercial fishermen in waters half a mile deep. Species found in cold waters in both the Atlantic and the Pacific may weigh more than 600 pounds, although they average less than half this exceptionally large size.

Intermediate in size are such species as the California Halibut (*Paralichthys californicus*), the Starry Flounder (*Platichthys stellatus*), and the American Plaice (*Hippoglossoides platessoides*). These, along with Summer and Winter flounders, Turbots and Dabs, are caught by both commercial fishermen and sport fishermen. They furnish great amounts of fun as well as good eating.

One of the most unusual features about flatfishes is their ability to change their collors to match their environment (see FISHES).

FLATWORMS are members of the phylum Platyhelminthes, which includes free-living flatworms (turbellarians), parasitic flukes, and tapeworms. Free-living flatworms live under rocks, among seaweeds, or in growth on pilings. Flatworms are so thin they are extremely hard to pick up except with a knife blade. Some swim near the surface at night and are attracted to lights.

Marine flatworms have broad, thin bodies with only one opening to the exterior. Some grow more than six inches in length. Algae sometimes live symbiotically in their tissues (see SYMBIOSIS). Other flatworms eat animals of various kinds, and because their bodies are so thin and nearly transparent, they are often

LIVER FLUKE
0.8 in.

PLANARIA
0.5 in.

Planaria is a free-living, fresh-water flatworm. Liver flukes are parasitic. Their eggs (1) are spread through wastes to water where they hatch into tiny larvae that infest snails (2). After a period of development, tailed larvae (3) leave the snail and bore through the skin and into the muscles of a fish (4). The larvae are transmitted to man or other animals through eating raw or poorly cooked fish (5).

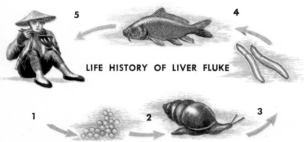

5   4

LIFE HISTORY OF LIVER FLUKE

1   2   3

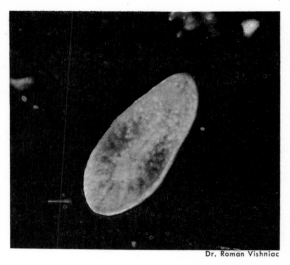

Dr. Roman Vishniac

Some free-living marine flatworms inhabit inshore waters; others drift with the plankton in the open sea.

colored by the food they eat. Some flatworms are brightly colored and may be spotted or striped. All have the ability to grow new parts (regenerate) when their bodies are damaged.

Liver flukes, which are mainly parasitic, reach a length of five or six inches. A saltwater ray caught on the Pacific Coast had one species in its body cavity, another in its mouth cavity, and a third on a copepod which was itself a parasite on the ray. They are commonly found on the gills of fishes. Generally saclike, they have one sucker surrounding their mouth and sometimes another in the middle of the body.

Swimmer's itch is caused by the larvae of a kind of flatworm. They usually bury themselves in the skin, especially beneath a bathing suit, and may cause severe itching for several days. In this case, the intermediate host is a snail that releases the flatworm larvae in visible clouds.

FLAX (*Linum usitatissimum*) is a strawlike annual that grows from one to four feet high in the three to five months before it is harvested. Linseed oil is obtained from the seeds, and linen fabrics are made from the fibers. Linen products range from such fine fabrics as cambric and damask to the coarse heavy-woven linen used in fire hoses and the strong twines used in sewing shoes.

FLAX

development of flowers
into ripe seeds

Linseed oil is produced by squeezing the oil from ripe
flax seeds. The oil is sometimes boiled.

When flax is grown for fiber, the plants are
pulled from the soil by hand or by machine.
The stems are submerged in water or spread
out in fields to rot from exposure to dew. This
is called "retting." After a time, the stems are
dried and run through rollers to break the
woody centers so they can be separated from
the bark containing the fibers. Bundles of flax
fibers are then carded and combed into fine
fibers that can be twisted into thread or woven
on a loom into fabrics.

The use of flax is ancient. Egyptian mum-
mies were clothed in linen cloth made of flax,
and paintings on the walls of tombs show the
culture and preparation of flax fibers.

Russia and the Baltic countries are now
the major flax producers. Ireland is the lead-
ing manufacturer of linen products.

In addition to Common Flax, from which
linen fibers come, there are many other kinds
of flax plants, a few of which are planted in
gardens. Some are blue-flowered like Common Flax; others are yellow, red, or white.
More than 40 kinds grow in North America.
Other colorful flax species come from Australia, New Zealand, Africa, and Europe.

FLEABANES (*Erigeron* spp.). Long ago
these daisy-family plants were thought to be
useful in controlling fleas, which is why they
are called fleabanes. Nowadays, fleabanes are
not a "bane" to anything except possibly to
farmers, for these common, colorful flowers
are sometimes so abundant that they are
considered noxious weeds.

Fleabanes are easily distinguished from
other daisies by their many very narrow,
petal-like rays. In other ways, including the
yellow central areas, their flowers are quite
daisy-like. Fleabanes are close relatives of
asters and resemble them. Their petal-like
rays vary from white to lavender or pink.

A few of the nearly 75 kinds of fleabanes
are tall, branched, weedy plants with small
whitish flowers. Whitetop or Daisy Fleabane
is common in pastures in eastern North
America. Several larger-flowered, attractive
kinds grow in western states, either on the
open plains or high in the mountains. Some
of the mountain species are so showy that
they are planted in rock gardens. A pretty
lavender fleabane known as the Seaside Daisy
grows at low elevations near the ocean along
the California coast. Another is found in
Alaska. Horseweeds, which grow 10 feet tall,
are common everywhere in North America
except northern Canada.

FLEABANES

DOG FLEA
Ctenocephalides canis
0.1 in.

FLEAS, small wingless insects of the order Siphonaptera, feed on the blood of warm-blooded animals. The body of a flea is flattened from side to side (compressed) and is covered with spines that project backwards. Both features allow the flea to move freely between an animal's hairs. Fleas can also move rapidly by jumping.

An infested animal may have many thousands of fleas on its body at one time. Although fleas feed on blood, they often spend much of their time off their host's body and can live several weeks or even longer without food. They leave the host to lay their eggs in cracks in the floor or in tiny crevices. Usually within two weeks the eggs hatch. Flea larvae are white, wormlike creatures without legs and less than a quarter of an inch long. They crawl about actively and feed on dried blood from the droppings of adult fleas and on other organic debris. The larval stage usually lasts two to four weeks, but if conditions are not favorable, it may last for several months. Then they spin silky cocoons to which dust or other dirt sticks so that the cocoons are hard to see. The pupal stage lasts about as long as the larval stage.

Most of the nearly 1,000 kinds of fleas live in the tropics. Fleas are important not only because of the discomfort they cause by biting man and his pets but also because they can transmit plague (sometimes called black death) and endemic typhus. Flea bites itch because of a substance in the flea's saliva that prevents the blood from coagulating.

Tropical chigoe fleas bury their heads in the flesh of their hosts, and may cause festering sores. They are common in the West Indies and South America. They are not the same as the chigger mite or redbug, which is a common pest in southern and central United States. (See MITES.)

FLIES, members of the order Diptera, never have more than one pair of wings, and nearly all have a pair of slender, knobbed structures, called halteres, in place of the second pair of wings. "Fly" is often used as a part of the name of many other insects. Butterfly, stonefly, mayfly, and dragonfly are examples. But in these the "fly" part of the name is used as part of the name to form a single word. When the "fly" part of the name is written as a separate word, as in flower fly or soldier fly, the insect is a true fly. There are many species of flies. Only the Coleoptera (beetles), Lepidoptera (moths, butterflies), and Hymeonoptera (bees, wasps, ants) are more abundant.

Flies develop by complete metamorphosis (egg, larva, pupa, and adult). The larvae of many kinds are called maggots. Some larvae are plant feeders that bore into stems or roots or tunnel through leaves. Some form galls (see GALLS). Others feed only on live animal flesh, and many eat decaying plants and animals. Adults eat plant juices or animal blood.

Although some kinds of flies are beneficial because they aid in pollinating flowers or are parasites of insect pests, the group as a whole is considered to be harmful. Many species are

This model of a House Fly's head shows numerous facets in the compound eyes and sponging mouth-parts.

American Museum of Natural History

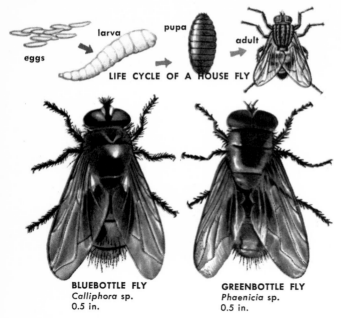

LIFE CYCLE OF A HOUSE FLY

eggs — larva — pupa — adult

BLUEBOTTLE FLY
Calliphora sp.
0.5 in.

GREENBOTTLE FLY
Phaenicia sp.
0.5 in.

pests of vegetable and fruit crops; others transmit such diseases as malaria, yellow fever, and sleeping sickness. (See INSECTS and also the index for listings of flies described separately in these volumes.)

FLOWER FLIES (Syrphidae) are a family of mostly colorful flies frequently seen around flowers. When disturbed, they hover and dart about rapidly. Many kinds are mimics of bees or wasps. They can neither bite nor sting, however, and most of them are really beneficial as pollinators.

Maggots of flower flies vary greatly in appearance and habitats. Larvae of the Drone Fly are called "rat-tailed maggots" because of the long breathing tube at the end of their abdomen. These maggots are usually abundant in highly polluted water, and they breathe by holding this tube above the surface. The larvae of some species of flower flies feed on aphids.

BEE FLY
Bombylius major
0.4 in.

SYRPHID FLY
Syrphus sp.
0.2 in.

FLOWERING PLANTS or Angiosperms produce seeds that are enclosed and protected by the ovary wall. They appeared in the Cretaceous and rapidly became the dominant plants on earth. Gymnosperms, the "naked seed" plants, meanwhile declined in numbers (see CONIFERS).

Early angiosperms included forms now extinct and also the earliest representatives of such surviving plants as oaks, maples, beeches, birches, figs, and others. With the coming of angiosperms, the earth was for the first time filled with colorful blossoms.

The Cenozoic history of the flowering plants shows continuous change and increasing modernization. Beautifully preserved leaf fossils are common in many areas. Ancient floral zones have been traced in great detail, and the known environments of similar living plant species have enabled geologists to determine the nature of the climate in many regions during Cenozoic times.

Development of flowering plants had a great effect on the history of various animal groups, especially mammals, birds, and insects. The spread of grass-covered prairies in Miocene times also produced widespread changes in habits and structure in many hoofed mammals.

Living angiosperms are the most successful of all plants. They exist from the tropics to polar areas, in wetlands and deserts. They range in size from a fraction of an inch to over 300 feet and occur in great profusion almost everywhere. In number of species, they outnumber all other living plants. We depend on them as direct and indirect sources of food, as do many other animals.

Flowering plants are divided into two groups: monocotyledons and dicotyledons. Monocotyledons have an undivided seed and produce only one seed leaf when they sprout. Grasses, palms, lilies, and orchids are among the more than 50,000 species of monocotyledons. Dicotyledon seeds are in two parts and produce two seed leaves when they sprout. There are about 200,000 species in this group. (See LIFE'S ORIGIN AND DEVELOPMENT; NON-FLOWERING PLANTS; PLANT KINGDOM.)

CATTAIL FAMILY *(Typhaceae)*—Cattails

WATER-PLANTAIN FAMILY *(Alismataceae)*—Arrowhead, Water Plantain

GRASS FAMILY *(Gramineae)*—Corn, Wheat, Rye, Oats, Bamboo, Sugar Cane, Bluegrass, Broomcorn, Timothy, Foxtail Grass

SEDGE FAMILY *(Cyperaceae)*—Sedge, Bulrush, Umbrella Plant, Spike Rush

PALM FAMILY *(Palmae)*—Coconut Palm, Date Palm, Raffia Palm, Rattan Palm

PINEAPPLE FAMILY *(Bromeliaceae)*—Pineapple, Long Moss

LILY FAMILY *(Liliaceae)*—Onion, Day Lily, Easter Lily, Dog's Tooth Violet, Star of Bethlehem, Hyacinth, Asparagus, Lily-of-the-valley, Trillium, Tulip, Tiger Lily, Garlic, Yucca

AMARYLLIS FAMILY *(Amaryllidaceae)*—Daffodil, Poet's Narcissus, Century Plant, Amaryllis

IRIS FAMILY *(Iridaceae)*—Iris, Blackberry Lily, Blue-eyed Grass

ORCHID FAMILY *(Orchidaceae)*—Showy Lady-slipper, Orchid, Vanilla, Moccasin Flower

WILLOW FAMILY *(Salicaceae)*—Willow, Poplar

BEECH FAMILY *(Fagaceae)*—Beech, Chestnut, Oak

NETTLE FAMILY *(Urticaceae)*—Elm, Mulberry, Nettle, Hackberry, Hemp, Hop, Osage Orange

GOOSEFOOT FAMILY *(Chenopodiaceae)* — Goosefoot, Beet, Spinach, Lamb's Quarters, Russian Thistle

PINK FAMILY *(Caryophyllaceae)*—Pink, Carnation, Catchfly, Bouncing Bet, Chickweed

WATER LILY FAMILY *(Nymphaeaceae)*—Water Lily, Pond Lily, Sacred Bean, Lotus

BUTTERCUP FAMILY *(Ranunculaceae)*—Buttercup, Meadow Rue, Hepatica, Anemone, Monkshood, Marsh Marigold, Baneberry, Columbine, Larkspur

POPPY FAMILY *(Papaveraceae)*—Poppy, Bloodroot, Prickly Poppy

MUSTARD FAMILY *(Cruciferae)*—Mustard, Sweet Alyssum, Peppergrass, Radish, Turnip, Cabbage, Watercress, Cauliflower, Shepherd's Purse, Toothwort

ROSE FAMILY *(Rosaceae)*—Rose, Spiraea, Hawthorn, Strawberry, Plum, Apple, Peach, Pear, Cherry, Blackberry, Raspberry

PEA FAMILY *(Leguminosae)*—Pea, Sweet Pea, Bean, Alfalfa, Clover, Lupine, Peanut, Locust, Honey Locust, Vetch, Kentucky Coffee Tree, Redbud

VIOLET FAMILY *(Violaceae)*—Violet, Pansy, Viola

PARSLEY FAMILY *(Umbelliferae)*—Parsley, Carrot, Parsnip, Celery, Queen Anne's Lace, Caraway, Dill, Poison Hemlock

HEATH FAMILY *(Ericaceae)*—Heather, Wintergreen, Indian Pipe, Rhododendron, Snowberry, Huckleberry, Blueberry, Cranberry, Trailing Arbutus, Azalea, Mountain Laurel.

PRIMROSE FAMILY *(Primulaceae)*—Primrose, Pimpernel, Loosestrife, Moneywort, Star Flower, Shooting Star, Featherfoil

MILKWEED FAMILY *(Asclepiadaceae)*—Milkweed, Butterfly Weed, Anglepod

MORNING GLORY FAMILY *(Convolvulaceae)*—Morning Glory, Bindweed, Dodder, Sweet Potato

MINT FAMILY *(Labiatae)*—Peppermint, Spearmint, Catnip, Sage, Horse Mint, Thyme, Horehound, Wild Marjoram, Salvia, Skullcap, Selfheal

NIGHTSHADE FAMILY *(Solanaceae)* — Nightshade, Bittersweet, Eggplant, Potato, Petunia, Tomato, Tobacco, Ground Cherry, Matrimony Vine

HONEYSUCKLE FAMILY *(Caprifoliaceae)* — Honeysuckle, Twinflower, Snowberry, High-bush Cranberry, Elder, Snowball

GOURD FAMILY *(Cucurbitaceae)* — Gourd, Pumpkin, Squash, Cucumber, Watermelon, Muskmelon

COMPOSITE FAMILY *(Compositae)*—Daisy, Sunflower, Aster, Goldenrod, Ragweed, Bachelor's Button, Dandelion, Marigold, Cosmos, Zinnia, Scotch Thistle, Lettuce, Coneflower

Yellow Hawkweed towers over white Fleabane, yellow Butter-and-eggs, and Red Clover in a summer meadow.

FLOWERS of many kinds add color and beauty to our world. Many are admired as they bloom wild in nature. Others are grown in flower gardens or indoor planters. Some have been carried far from their original homes and have been used to develop countless new varieties far more handsome than their wild ancestors. The origin of some familiar flowers is shown in the map on page 470. The many wild and cultivated flowers described and illustrated in these volumes represent a few of the 250,000 kinds of flowering plants that grow throughout the world.

Flowers have developed in only one large group of plants, the angiosperms or flowering plants. No other plants have flowers. Flowers may vary in form and size, but they all have one function—to produce fruits and seeds. Many other kinds of plants reproduce by the fusion of male and female cells, but only in the angiosperms are the egg cells (ovules) in a protective organ (the ovary) which matures to become a fruit. (See FLOWERING PLANTS.)

Without blossoms most plants we know would disappear sooner or later because most of them grow from seeds, and seeds develop from flowers. Many of the fruits and vegetables that are an important part of our daily food supply are formed by and from flowers.

Apples, oranges, grapes and the like come from blossoms. So do many vegetables, like peas, beans, and tomatoes, and all of the cereal grains, such as wheat, barley, oats, rice, and corn. These are the most important plant crops in the world. Without them the human race could not survive, nor could many other animals. Some flowers and flower buds are eaten directly. The artichoke is the flower bud of a thistle; broccoli and cauliflower are also flower buds. In many countries squash blossoms are sold in markets.

Flowers yield nearly all the perfumes which women use. These delicate odors are extracted from acres upon acres of flowers. Flowers are important in religious services. We use them to honor the living and the dead. We admire flowers for their beauty, and without them our world would be an unhappy, very difficult place in which to live.

Flowers grow nearly everywhere. A few kinds even grow in the ocean. Others live on hot desert sands. Early crocuses and snow lilies sometimes bloom while spring snows are still on the ground. In spring, summer, and fall, flowers of many kinds and colors bloom in fields, forests, open plains, and high in mountains. Many flowers grow in the tropics and quite a few in polar regions.

PARTS OF A FLOWER

Flowers usually have four important parts: sepals, petals, pistils, and stamens. All of the sepals together are called the calyx, and all of the petals together form the corolla. The sepals, generally green, are at the base of the flower. Immediately above them are the colorful petals which give the flower its beauty and help to attract insects. These two parts are not the essential parts of the flower, however. Actually the stamens and the pistil are the parts needed for making seeds. These sepals and petals are only colorful decorations surrounding these important parts.

Most stamens consist of a slim filament, or stalk, on top of which is a pouch called the anther which contains the tiny pollen grains. Stamens are the male parts of the flower. The vase-shaped pistil in the center of the flower is the female part. Its swollen base is the ovary containing one or more eggs, or ovules.

Flowers which have both stamens and pistils are called *perfect* flowers. Flowers which lack either stamens or pistils are called *imperfect*. Perfect flowers may pollinate themselves, but most commonly the pollen is brought from other flowers nearby. This is *cross-pollination*. Pollen is either carried to flowers by the wind or is brought by insects that come for the flower's nectar. Some insects, especially bees and moths, have special adaptations for pollinating flowers.

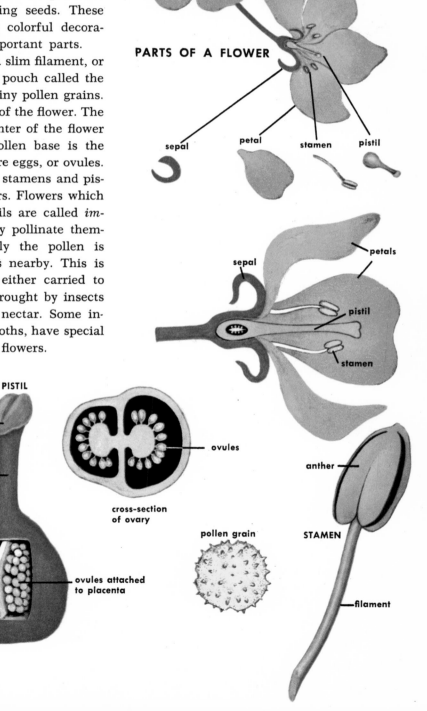

PARTS OF A FLOWER

sepal   petal   stamen   pistil

sepal   petals   pistil   stamen

PISTIL

stigma — style — ovary —

ovules attached to placenta

cross-section of ovary

ovules

pollen grain

anther —

STAMEN

filament

fertilized ovules developing inside the ovary

TYPES OF FLOWER ARRANGEMENTS ON STEMS

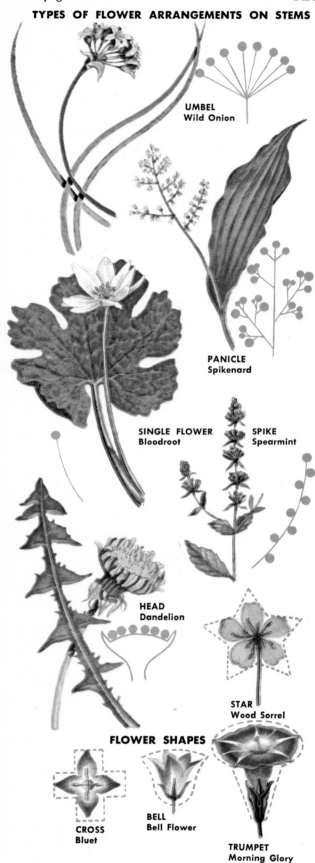

UMBEL
Wild Onion

PANICLE
Spikenard

SINGLE FLOWER
Bloodroot

SPIKE
Spearmint

HEAD
Dandelion

STAR
Wood Sorrel

FLOWER SHAPES

CROSS
Bluet

BELL
Bell Flower

TRUMPET
Morning Glory

FORMS OF FLOWERS

There are many different types of flowers. Buttercups, for example, have many small pistils in each flower instead of just one. Waterlilies also have a number of pistils at the center where the petals are attached. Morning-glory flowers have their petals united into a tube like a colorful trumpet. Sweetpea blooms have their petals partly united.

The various shapes and colors of flowers and the way their parts are united are useful in identifying flowers. Where and when the flowers grow is also a help. Some bloom in spring; others in summer or fall.

Still another means of identification is the way the flowers are borne on the plant's branches. Small flowers often grow in special clusters; some of them flat-topped, some rounded, and others arranged in long sprays or spires. Finally, the leaves of the plant and their placement on the stem are a help in identification, too.

ORIGIN OF FLOWERS

Many attractive flowers have been taken from their native land to other parts of the world and developed as garden flowers. Cultivated geraniums, for example, came from Africa, where many kinds still grow wild. The African Violet has many close relatives still living in the mountains of South Africa. Easter Lilies grow wild in Asia, while the Carnation, Candytuft, Crocus, Pansy, Snapdragon, and Wallflower came from Europe.

North America has contributed its share of cultivated flowers. The California Poppy, Louisiana Iris, and several kinds of rhododendrons and azaleas originated in the United States. Poinsettias, dahlias, zinnias, marigolds, and cosmos came from Mexico.

Some cultivated flowers are exactly the same as the wild forms. Most have been crossed and new cultivated forms developed by hybridization. Cultivated flowers may need extra care, watering or protection as they are grown under conditions quite different from their wild ancestors. Lacking proper care, many cultivated varieties could not survive in competition with native species.

(1) Rhododendron, (2) Louisiana Iris, (3) Snapdragon, (4) Pansy, (5) Wallflower, (6) Crocus, (7) Anemone, (8) Tulip, (9) Chinese Aster, (10) Japanese Iris, (11) Zinnia, (12) California Poppy, (13) Carnation, (14) Regal Lily, (15) Dahlia, (16) Marigold, (17) Cosmos, (18) Sweetpea, (19) Candytufts, (20) Oriental Poppy, (21) Hollyhock, (22) Poinsettia, (23) Morning Glory, (24) Canna, (25) Bird-of-Paradise Flower, (26) Lobelia, (27) Strawflower, (28) Nasturtium, (29) Petunia, (30) Fuchsia, (31) Gladiola, (32) Geranium, (33) Calla Lily, (34) Hibiscus, (35) Chrysanthemum.

INSECT POLLINATION

Flowers that depend on insects to pollinate them do not produce as much pollen, but the pollen grains are larger. Often the grains are sticky or have hooking devices that cling easily to an insect's body. Many flowers have unusual arrangements which help bring about pollination by insects. An example is Salvia (see SAGE), a common flower of European and American gardens. Its flower petals are shaped in such a way that when a heavy insect, such as a bee, lights on the lower petal, it pushes against a lever that lowers the anther and dusts off pollen on its back. The bee brushes the pollen off on the stigma of the next flower as it enters, as the drooping stigma scrapes its back.

The color of flowers may attract insects. Often the color of flowers range into the

When a bee enters a young Salvia flower (left), it pushes against the base of the stamens and causes them to pivot forward, the anthers depositing pollen on the hairs of the bee's back. Later the bee visits an older flower (right) in which the stigma has developed and bent downward. Pollen picked up earlier from younger flowers is deposited on the stigma of the pistil, thus accomplishing cross-pollination.

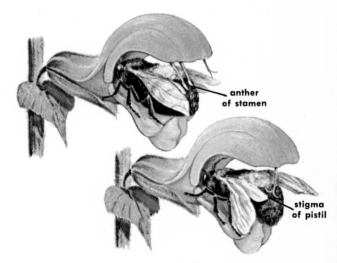

anther of stamen

stigma of pistil

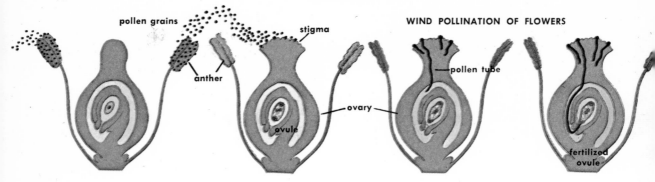

WIND POLLINATION OF FLOWERS

ultraviolet end of the spectrum. These short rays are visible to insects but not to the human eye. Thus a flower that appears white to a human may be blue or violet to a bee or other insect visitor. (See COLOR.)

Some night-blooming flowers depend on insects for pollination. Color is of no value in the dark, so it is not surprising that night-blooming flowers are yellow or white. Their fragrance guides moths or other night-flying insects to them.

Some flowers are constructed to discourage visits by insects that would steal nectar without transferring pollen. Ants, for example, are not good pollinators, nor are most beetles. They have smooth bodies to which the pollen does not cling. Stems of many flowers are covered with a dense growth of hairs or bristles so that it is hard for these crawling insects to get to the flowers.

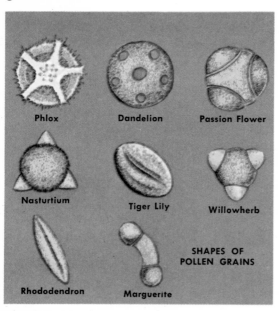

SHAPES OF POLLEN GRAINS

Phlox, Dandelion, Passion Flower, Nasturtium, Tiger Lily, Willowherb, Rhododendron, Marguerite

Cross-pollination by the wind is a common way in which flowers are fertilized. Pollen is shed from the anthers when they are ripe (1). At this stage, in most flowers, the pistil has not yet matured. The pollen is blown by the wind and lands on the roughened or sticky stigma (2) of another flower in which the anthers have withered and the pistil has matured. In this flower, the ovary is ripe, and the ovules are ready to be fertilized. The pollen grains germinate, the tubules growing down through the style toward the ovules (3). Male cells unite with the ovules, which will ripen as seeds. The fruit consists of the seeds surrounded by the fleshy parts of the ovary.

POLLINATION AND FERTILIZATION

The flower's job is reproduction—the making of seeds from which new plants will grow. Reproduction begins with pollination.

Soon after a pollen grain lands on the stigma, the flattened and often sticky top of the pistil, it develops a tiny tube that grows downward into the base of the pistil. Through this tube passes the male cell which fertilizes the egg. The fertilized egg is the very first stage of a new plant. Finally, most parts of the flower dry up and fall off, leaving only the pistil with its fertilized ovules. These develop into seeds which in proper conditions sprout and become new plants.

Many plants are capable of self-fertilization, but in cross-pollination the plants produced are different from both parents. These variations may enable some plants to survive in conditions which neither parent could tolerate. Cross-pollination also produces the greatest variety of colors and forms.

Most pollen grains are transferred either by the wind or by insects. Flowers pollinated by the wind often produce many millions of pollen grains, for the chances of a grain of pollen reaching the proper blossoms are indeed slim. Pollen grains carried by the wind have shapes that help keep them air-borne. They may drift many miles. Few wind-pollinated flowers are showy or have a sweet odor, as this would have no advantage to the plant. Their stigmas are generally broad with a hairy or sticky surface. Grasses and many kinds of trees are pollinated by the wind.

Flowers that depend on insects to pollinate them often have bright petals and pleasant odors. Many kinds of insects—bees, wasps, moths, butterflies, beetles, flies, and others—may transfer the pollen from one flower to another. They do not visit the flowers for this purpose but come for the sweet nectar, which is a food for them. Bees, however, also use the pollen for food.

Man is a pollinator, too. He creates new flowers by transferring the pollen from one flower to another, forming hybrid or cross-bred flowers of new colors, sizes and shapes. The hybrid flower may be far more beautiful than the original. Most cultivated flowers are a result of hybridizing.

FLUORITE, a calcium fluoride, occurs in cubic crystals, or cubes with beveled corners. Though its usual color is purple or green, it may be colorless or any color. It has a white streak and a glassy luster. Fluorite usually is found as a hydrothermal replacement mineral and occurs in both igneous and sedimentary rocks. Because it makes slag more fluid and helps to remove phosphorus and sulfur, fluorite is added to iron ore in the open-hearth smelting to make steel and also in the smelting of other ores. Hydrofluoric acid—made from fluorite—is used to dissolve silica or to etch glass. Freon gas, also made of fluorite, is a refrigerant in electric refrigerators. Some telescope and spectroscope lenses are made of clear, flawless fluorite because of its low index of refraction and dispersion. Some fluorite is used in enamels and glass. Fluorite comes from Illinois, Kentucky, Colorado, Utah, and Nevada.

Another fluorite mineral is cryolite. It is associated with pegmatites and granite in snow-white compact masses.

FLYCATCHERS form a family of birds widespread throughout the Western Hemisphere. From a perch they watch for passing insects, their only food, and dart out to catch them. When they snap a bug, their bills make a loud click. When frost kills the insects, the flycatchers migrate to a warmer climate. Many kinds breed in North America, but almost all flycatchers winter in Central and South America. Flycatchers build nests anywhere from the ground to the tops of high trees, depending on the species. They lay from three to six eggs.

Crested Flycatchers build large nests in any convenient hole—in hollow trees, in open-ended R.F.D. mail boxes, or even in discarded stovepipes. Usually a cast off snake skin is woven into the nest. The reason for the snake skin is a mystery to man.

The Kingbird gave flycatchers their reputation as tyrants all over the Western Hemisphere. American Indians called the Kingbird "little chief." When protecting its nesting territory, the Kingbird, though only nine inches long, does not hesitate to attack crows, owls, hawks, or even eagles. It dives on its enemy and pecks at its head with its sharp bill. An angry Kingbird will ride on the back of a fleeing crow. Only tiny hummingbirds, too swift to catch, are safe in the vicinity of a nesting Kingbird. Kingbirds even attack people who approach their nests. Kingbirds are also called "bee martins," for they have no fear of stings and consider an apiary a fine place to feed.

Fork-tailed Flycatchers of Mexico, Central and South America have habits like those of other flycatchers—plus a peculiar habit of their own. Every evening at sunset all the

crystal

FLUORITE
Southern Illinois

VERMILION FLYCATCHER—5.5 in.
Pyrocephalus rubinus
Southwestern U.S. to Honduras

SCISSOR-TAILED FLYCATCHER—15 in.
Muscivora forficata
South-central United States

EASTERN KINGBIRD—9 in.
Tyrannus tyrannus
Central and eastern North America

GREAT CRESTED FLYCATCHER—9 in.
Myiarchus crinitis
Eastern North America

EASTERN PHOEBE—7
Sayornis phoebe
Eastern North America

Fork-tails in an area go to the top of the highest trees and call excitedly. Then they fly in a group high into the air and circle for a few minutes. Uttering sharp cries, they drop down in a wild zigzag flight, separate into pairs, and return to their original treetops.

Scissor-tailed Flycatchers have longer tails than any other North American birds their size. They breed in south-central and southeastern United States but are wandering birds found almost everywhere except in high mountain country. The Scissor-tailed Flycatcher is the state bird of Oklahoma.

Phoebes are early-bird flycatchers—first to arrive at their breeding grounds in spring and first to sing in the morning. They often build their mud and moss nests under small bridges over running water where insects are thick.

Vermilion Flycatchers are familiar from just north of the Mexican border through Central America. The Mexican name for the bird is *brasita de fuego* ("little coal of fire"), an appropriate name for the males which are the brightest of the flycatchers.

FLYING ANIMALS. Only insects, birds, and bats have wings and are true flying animals. Pteranodons, extinct reptiles, were the only other animals capable of flight.

Other animals have developed an ability to glide. They spread folds of skin attached to their front and hind legs to serve as sails. Flying lizards of the East Indies, some African rodents, a small Australian opossum, and flying squirrels are gliders. When a flying squirrel glides, it holds its tail in a horizontal position and spreads its legs to stretch the skin folds outward. It may soar for 100 yards. To stop, it jerks its tail upward as a brake and pulls in its legs. It lands softly on a branch. In "flight" it can change direction quickly by varying the slack in its "wings" and by raising its tail as a rudder.

Some fish are also gliders. Flyingfish, usually found in warmer ocean waters, vibrate their tails in the water to gain speed, then use their winglike fins to glide upward. They can soar for several hundred feet just above the surface of the sea.

Insects' wings are outgrowths of the body wall. They are powered by complicated muscles. Many insects can hover, fly backwards, or make right-angle turns. Most insects have two pairs of wings. One of the remarkable things about insects' wings is the speed with which they can move. Although those of a House Fly move only about 15 to 50 vibrations per second, those of a mosquito beat 400 to 500 times per second and of a midge 1,000 times per second. Dragonflies can fly 50 miles per hour for short distances, and locusts are capable of flying five to eight hours without stopping.

The energy used for short flights is obtained from sugar. An exhausted fruit fly can resume flight within 30 seconds after feeding on sugar water. Bees may forage several miles for nectar, which is about 70 per cent sugar, but long trips are not economical since the bees use most of the sugar for fuel during their return flight.

The streamlined bodies of birds are made buoyant by lightweight hollow bones that contain air sacs connected to their lungs.

FLYING FROG
Rhacophorus reinwardtii

The "flying frog" of Asia used the broad webs on its feet as parachutes to glide from overhead branches.

GREEN DARNER
Anax junius

Dragonflies fly faster than other insects and catch their food on the wing.

"Flying snakes" of Asia deflate their lungs and lift their ribs, thus flattening their body for gliding.

FLYING SNAKE
Chrysopelea sp.

FLYING DRAGON
Draco sp.

Loose folds of skin stretched over extra-long ribs make the gliding "wings" of these Asiatic lizards.

FLYING SQUIRREL
Glaucomys sp.

Flying squirrels use their tail as a brake to stop a glide or as a rudder to change direction.

Squids may leap from the water and glide through the air for 50 or 60 yards on their outstretched fins.

FLYING SQUID
Onychoteuthis sp.

Powerful flight muscles are attached to the keel, an extension of the breastbone, and the bird's feathered tail serves as a rudder and brake. The Frigate-bird, a tropical soaring sea bird, has a wingspan of seven feet but weighs only a couple of pounds. Its bones account for only four ounces of its weight.

Birds that take off from the ground or a tree nearly always do so into the wind. If you walk with the wind toward a flock of sparrows on the ground, they will fly first into the wind —toward you—before veering away. Many birds cannot take off into a tail wind. Those capable of long flight (such as ducks, loons, herons, cranes) usually trail their legs behind, but perching birds (crows, sparrows, warblers, and others) draw their legs up and forward, ready for instant landing.

Soaring birds have a very large tail-wing surface as compared to wing-flapping forms. Gulls have long narrow wings, while hawks have short, broad wings. These birds use air currents and updrafts to sustain their flight.

Speeds and altitudes attained by birds are frequently exaggerated. Pheasants can fly at about 35 miles per hour, starlings about 50, and vultures have been recorded at 110. Most birds do not exceed an altitude of 3,000 feet. The Andean Condor nests at 16,000 feet, and a bird similar to a cowbird has been observed at 27,000 feet on Mt. Everest.

Hummingbirds are noted for their ability to "stand still" in the air and to fly backward. Their wings appear as a blur, yet they vibrate only about 60 to 75 times per second, considerably slower than some insects. Pigeons flap their wings about 8 times per second.

Bats are the only flying mammals. Their front legs are greatly modified as wings but are quite different from the wings of birds. Their fingers are elongated and webbed with a thin skin membrane that extends to the hind legs and may include the tail. Bats are capable of very quick changes in direction while in flight. They avoid objects as a result of echoes from their high-pitched sounds. They catch insects in flight and even drink on the wing, picking up a "tongueful" of water as they skim over the surface.

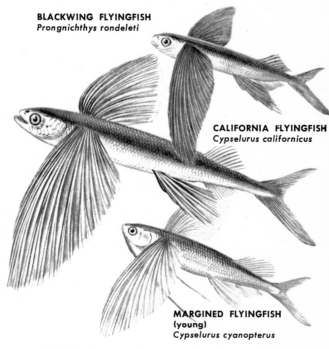

FOUR-WINGED FLYINGFISH
Cypselurus heterurus

FLYINGFISHES (*Cypselurus* spp.) are small fishes that live close to the surface in the deep waters of warm seas. They feed on smaller fishes and are, in turn, important food for larger surface feeders, such as tunas, mackerels, and Dolphins. To escape, they swim rapidly, turn upward suddenly and shoot into the air. Occasionally they "fly" for long distances. More often they are airborne only a few seconds at a time in glides of 50 yards or less. Their broad pectoral fins—and in some species the pelvic fins, too—are their wings. California Flyingfish reach a length of 18 inches; most species are less than 12 inches long.

BLACKWING FLYINGFISH
Prongnichthys rondeleti

CALIFORNIA FLYINGFISH
Cypselurus californicus

MARGINED FLYINGFISH
(young)
Cypselurus cyanopterus

FLYING LEMURS (*Galeopithecus* spp. and *Galeopterus* spp.) are found in the tropical forests from Malaya to the Philippines. They are more closely related to shrews than to monkey-like lemurs. They are not capable of true flight, as are bats, but are excellent gliders. By spreading the thin membrane between their neck, legs, and tail, they can sail 200 feet or more from one tree to another, losing only about a foot of altitude for every five feet of the glide. These soft-furred, squirrel-sized animals, also called Colugos, are

nearly helpless on the ground and are unable to stand erect. Adults are shades of brown or gray; some are dappled with small, white spots. Their nearly naked ears are pinkish.

FLYING LIZARDS (*Draco* spp.) are slender 10-inch tree lizards of the agamid family. About 40 species live in the jungles of the East Indies and southeastern Asia. They have wide flaps of skin stretched between their front and hind legs, and several long ribs also project into the webs to give them support. When the flaps are spread wide, the lizards can glide from high in a tree to the ground or to a lower spot on other trees or vegetation. They do not flap these "wings" but are expert gliders. The flaps are brightly colored, but the remainder of the body is drab. Because these lizards do not live well in captivity, they are not often seen in zoos.

FLYING LEMUR
Galeopithecus sp.
18 in. long

FOAMFLOWER

FOAMFLOWERS (*Tiarella cordifolia*) grow in moist, rich woodlands of cool regions in North America and eastern Asia. Their hairy, maple-like leaves, which grow close to the ground, become purplish-green to bronze in autumn. Clusters of white flowers on long spikes appear in early spring. Each tiny seed resembles a crown or tiara. Another name for Foamflower is False Miterwort.

FOOD CHAINS. Every living thing has the problem of acquiring food to satisfy its own needs, and nearly every living thing becomes food for one or more other organisms. The sequence of one life form depending on another is called a food chain.

All food chains depend basically on plants. Plant-eating animals become food for flesh eaters, some of which are eaten by other flesh eaters. Plants or animals that die are decomposed to basic elements and compounds.

All the earth's energy is derived from the sun. It is the green, growing plant world that harnesses the energy and makes it available to animal life. Less than 3 per cent of the solar energy is turned into food by the plants, however. Only a small fraction of the food of an animal is converted into body protoplasm. Each step in a food chain involves a further loss of energy. It has been estimated that about 18,000 pounds of alfalfa are required to produce 200 pounds of beef. This is just sufficient to meet the meat requirements of a 80- or 90-pound child for one year. Similarly, it is estimated that about 10,000 pounds of microscopic plants have to be eaten to provide about one pound of tuna for the table. Only about a tenth of this pound of tuna is added to the body weight of the person who eats the fish.

Most larger fishes eat smaller fishes that eat still smaller animals, such as copepods (crustaceans). These scarcely visible animals, in turn, feed on diatoms or other tiny algae that form the sea's plankton.

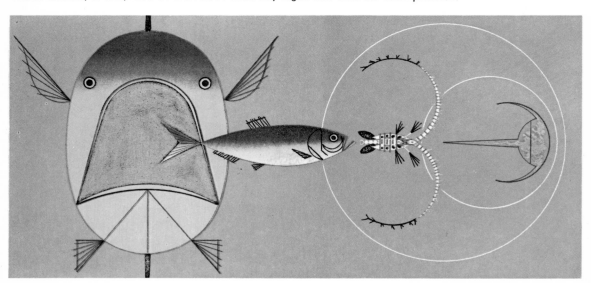

Royal Ontario Museum (Canada)

American Indians built corrals into which bison (buffalo) were driven for easy slaughter.

FOODS OF MAN. Men of the Old Stone Age got their food by digging, gathering, trapping, and hunting. Meals must have included meat from various animals, fruits, roots, grubs, shellfish, and carrion.

Hunting and food gathering peoples must know much about their environment. To find wild roots and edible seeds and to trap food animals takes knowledge of their habits, the seasons, the favorable places, and ways of preparing and preserving what is found. Devices must be made for digging the roots and for catching the game. To bring down his game, primitive man devised clubs, spears, arrows, darts, traps of all kinds, nets, hooks, axes, knives, and poisons. To approach his game he learned how to stalk and also how to use boats and to ride horses. The tracking and stalking of game were developed into a real science. Eskimos dress in sealskin clothing and approach the seal by imitating its movements. Hunting certain animals calls for group action. In hunting the American bison or buffalo, the Plains Indians not only organized for the hunt but had a police force to see that everyone did his job as expected.

Antelope and rabbit hunting was also highly organized under the authority of a "rabbit" or "antelope" boss. Africans, too, conduct skillful and courageous group hunts in trapping such fierce animals as the elephant. Usually, hunting tribes divide up into small bands, each roaming its part of the tribal territory. When the game in one place gives out, they move on for better hunting.

Disguised as animals, these Indian hunters are approaching a herd of bison that would otherwise flee.

American Museum of Natural History

FISHING

Angling, or catching fish by hook and line, is an ancient art. Fishhooks made of bone have been found with the remains of Old Stone Age Man. A later improvement in the fishhook was the barb. This prevents the fish from slipping off the hook after it has been hooked. The "gorge" was probably used even before the hook. This is a sharp instrument of stone or metal fixed inside the bait at the end of a line. It lodged crosswise in the fish's gullet when the bait was swallowed and the line was pulled taut.

Nets have been made in many shapes and sizes, each designed for a specific kind of fishing. Modern nets do not differ greatly from nets made and used by primitive man. Fish may also be captured by shooting them with a spear or arrow, by trapping them, and even by doping and by tickling them. A Chinese system of fishing is to train cormorants to bring in the live fish. South American Indians used crushed derris roots (rotenone) to poison fish without making them inedible.

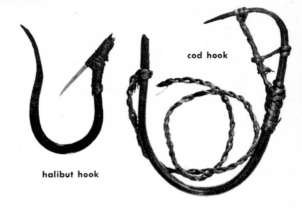

cod hook

halibut hook

Indians made fishhooks of wood, bone, and horn.

Frequently several methods of fishing are used at the same time. Thus the Indians of the Pacific Northwest built dams across streams to slow down the salmon as they swam upstream to spawn. When the salmon got stalled below the dam, the Indians could spear or net them easily.

TRAPS

Since the early Old Stone Age man has used traps to catch animals less clever than himself. All recent primitive peoples and many civilized ones use traps for getting food, skins, and other useful products and also to do away with undesirable animals. There are scores of different kinds of traps.

These Indians are netting, trapping, and smoking salmon during a spawning run at a falls in the Pacific Northwest.

Fishermen are using a trap or weir made of rushes to catch fish from this lake in Uganda in equatorial Africa.

The simplest trap is a pit dug along an animal trail and hidden by branches. Sometimes sharp posts are set in the bottom to pierce the animal when it drops in. "Deadfalls" are traps in which the animal pulls the enclosure down over him when he tugs at a bait. Wolves are caught by setting up two circular fences, one inside the other and with a narrow circular passageway between the two. A door in the outer fence stands open. The wolf goes through the door into the passageway and goes around the circle. When he comes to the open door, he pushes it closed and cannot pull it open again.

"Snares" catch animals as they move forward. The animal pushes his head into a noose which tightens and holds him. A "spring trap" is a noose tied to a bent tree or a branch. The branch is weighted down, but when the animal is inside the noose, the weight is released so that the bent tree straightens up suddenly and the animal swings into space.

Many peoples trap fish. One method involves the use of a large basket. A funnel, with its large opening toward the outside, is fitted into one end of the basket. Fish find their way into the basket through the big end but rarely find the opening to escape.

The Pomo Indians of coastal California were experts at making nets, used to catch birds as well as fish.

Before man developed the skill that made him a formidable hunter, he had to rely on food that could not run from him. Insects, mollusks, and the products of the plant kingdom were of greater importance to him than the animals that he could not catch.

Fruits, berries, roots, and succulent stems must have been available everywhere. The first human groups probably resembled those of the present-day Australian aborigines. They were wandering family units that subsisted on whatever edible chanced their way, and they returned each season to former camps near to some ripening wild crop or easily harvested grain.

The art of cooking increased the scope of man's diet. Heat renders many plant products soft and palatable that are useless when raw, and increases their digestibility.

Recognition of the connection between the seed and the plant led early man to propagate desirable species. In his wanderings, the more edible plants became spread over wide areas in this fashion. Agriculture, the careful planting and tending of crops, was a much later development in the history of the human race. (See AGRICULTURE.)

One of the by-products of efficient transportation on land and on the oceans was the spread of useful plants. Emigrants carried familiar species to their new homes, and explorers scoured new lands for potentially valuable plants. People of today may choose from a world-wide garden.

FOOTLESS LIZARD
10 in.

FOOTLESS LIZARDS (*Anniella pulchra*) of western North America in California and Baja California are smooth-scaled, earless, and completely limbless lizards that live in sandy soils. Often they burrow in the top few inches where they find their insect food by smell or touch. Their eyes are greatly reduced and covered with small, movable lids.

FORESTS are communities of trees and shrubs, but they are also communities of flowers, fungi, insects, reptiles, birds, mammals, soil, moisture, and air. Trees are, however, the dominant type of life in forests.

Forests of the world are divided into three broad classes: boreal conifers, temperate hardwoods, and tropical hardwoods. Boreal conifers (cone-bearing trees) are located in cool temperate climates. They form a belt encircling the earth just below the treeless arctic tundra. In the northern part are chiefly spruces and firs. The southern part contains also pines, larches, and hemlocks.

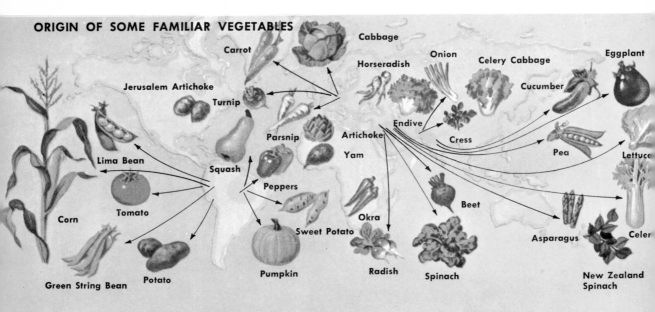

ORIGIN OF SOME FAMILIAR VEGETABLES

Corn · Green String Bean · Lima Bean · Tomato · Potato · Jerusalem Artichoke · Carrot · Turnip · Parsnip · Squash · Peppers · Sweet Potato · Pumpkin · Cabbage · Horseradish · Artichoke · Yam · Okra · Radish · Onion · Endive · Cress · Beet · Spinach · Celery Cabbage · Cucumber · Eggplant · Pea · Lettuce · Asparagus · Celery · New Zealand Spinach

Temperate hardwood forests are made up of deciduous trees—those that shed their leaves in the fall. The forests consist of many species of ash, basswood, beech, birch, elm, maple, and oak. Hardwoods also grow in tropical lowlands and include such valuable and beautiful trees as ebony, mahogany, and rosewood.

Of approximately 650 million acres of useful forest lands in the United States, about 130 million acres are publicly owned. The remainder are owned chiefly by lumber companies, paper mills, and farmers. About 49 billion board feet of lumber is cut annually.

Forests provide lumber for construction and wood pulp for paper. They regulate and conserve water necessary for other plants, for animals, and for irrigation, power, and drinking water supplies. They reinforce the soil and decrease the force of rainfall and runoff, thus helping to prevent erosion. Forests also affect temperature, preventing it from dropping as low at night or going as high during the day as in grasslands. They also serve as windbreaks that cut the force of sweeping winds. In deep forests the air is absolutely still. Forests convert tremendous amounts of sun energy into food, thus serving as the first link in the food chain of plant-animal communities. Fewer animals live in deep forests, however, than in more open country. The greatest variety and abundance of animal life is at the forest edge. (See TREES.)

FORGET-ME-NOTS (*Myosotis* spp.) have been favorite flowers for centuries. They are mentioned often in legends and in poetry and are regarded as symbols of friendship and trust. They are a number of species adapted to a wide range of habitats.

Forget-me-nots are common in Europe, Asia, and North America. Several species grow wild, and cultivated varieties often escape gardens and grow wild, too. Forget-me-nots are partial to shady, moist places. Some of the wild kinds grow in swampy areas, even partly submerged in water. In some regions, roadside slopes are colored blue by masses of their blossoms.

Their usual color is pale blue with a white or a white-and-yellow center, but some are white, pink, or even yellow. A low-growing type is often used as an edging in gardens or along sidewalks.

FORGET-ME-NOT
Myosotis scorpioides

FORSYTHIAS (*Forsythia* spp.) are shrubs native to China and are grown throughout the world as ornamentals. Another common name for them is Golden Bells. In early spring before their leaves appear they bear yellow, bell-shaped flowers. Some grow tall (8 to 10 ft.) and have erect stems; others have droopy, willowy branches. Often these popular shrubs are planted to form a flowering hedge. Forsythias are members of the olive family which includes such other ornamentals as Lilacs, Jasmines, and Privets.

FORSYTHIA
Forsythia intermedia spectabilis

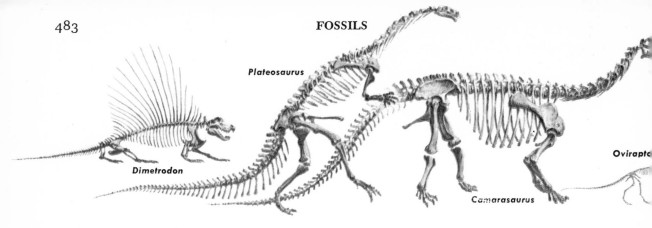

Dimetrodon
Plateosaurus
Camarasaurus
Ovirapto

FOSSILS are the actual remains of prehistoric animals and plants or some direct evidence of their existence. They may be bones or shells of animals, imprints of leaves and stems of plants, or just trails or borings made by worms in wet mud or sand that was later changed into rock. Some fossils are very old—far older than the oldest men.

In rare cases whole animals have been preserved. In 1846, a young Russian surveyor

The remains of many Ice Age animals have been found in the La Brea Tar Pits in Los Anaeles, California.

CONDORS
Teratornis merriami

DIRE WOLF
Canis dirus

SABER-TOOTHS
Smilodon californicu

EMPEROR MAMMOTH
Mammuthus imperator

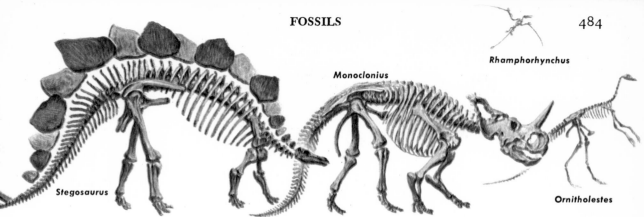

Stegosaurus

Monoclonius

Rhamphorhynchus

Ornitholestes

was exploring the Indigirka River in Siberia. As his party reached a place where a stream, swollen by recent heavy rains, had undercut the river bank, he noticed a huge, dark object floating in the water. It was a Woolly Mammoth, its heavy tusks still preserved, its eyes still open, its shaggy coat still soft, its trunk swaying in the water. This creature had lived 10,000 years ago, when most of northern Europe was covered by glaciers.

A party of 50 men and their horses managed to drag the great beast onto the bank. They found that even the contents of the animal's stomach had been refrigerated in the frozen ground of the arctic country.

Since that first discovery numbers of other animals have been found similarly preserved by deep freezing in Siberia and Alaska. In Galicia, Poland, a complete Woolly Rhinoceros was discovered, the soft parts of its body preserved in the oil-soaked ground.

Spectacular as these examples are, they are very rare. The soft parts of most fossils either are not preserved at all or are preserved only as films or impressions. In dry caves in Nevada and Patagonia, remains of Ground Sloths have been found with dried skin, hair and tendons preserved. In parts of western Canada, the delicate patterns of dinosaur skin have been preserved as impressions in sandstone, formed from sand that covered the dried-out carcasses.

Amber, the fossil resin of trees, sometimes contains perfectly preserved insects and leaves. Most of these come from the Baltic region of Europe, but a few have been found in Alaska and Mexico. Even the delicate wings and tiny hairs of the insects are intact.

Carbonized Fern Leaf

Fossil Trilobite (cast)

Insect Preserved in Amber

A frozen Woolly Mammoth, found in Siberia in 1900.

In recent rocks, as in Florida, many fossil shells are preserved intact. *Arca*, much like living species, is about one million years old.

PETRIFIED WOOD

ARCA

Cells of the wood of auracaria pines that grew more than 150 million years ago in Arizona have been replaced by silica, preserving details in agate.

The soft tissues of most fossils are preserved only as dark films of carbon or, more often, as black outlines on the rock. Leaves of trees which made up the mighty coal-forming forests are preserved in this way. So are some animals, such as the giant fish-lizards (icthyosaurs) known from Germany.

But all these examples are rarities. Usually fossils represent only the hard parts of ancient animals and plants, whose soft parts decayed soon after their death. In a few cases these hard parts are not much altered. In the famous Rancho La Brea tar pits in Los Angeles, California, bones of many ice-age animals were preserved by burial in asphalt, which sealed and protected them. It is not difficult to imagine how the cries of a Mammoth caught in the tar would bring Saber-toothed Cats or carrion-loving condors quickly to the scene. And then they, too, would become engulfed in the clinging asphalt. Even mice, small birds, and plants were trapped in the treacherous, seeping tar.

Not all fossils with unaltered hard parts were preserved under such dramatic conditions. Shellfish left their shells as records. Some marine worms have tiny jaw pieces made of chitin, a horny substance so resistant to change that specimens 500 million years old are still flexible and unaltered.

More commonly the pore spaces in wood, bone, and shell are filled up by substances, usually silica or lime, deposited from water filtering through the sand and mud in which they were buried. Sometimes all the original material is dissolved and is completely replaced by these new materials. Usually this destroys whatever fine structure the original may have had, but occasionally even the most minute cellular structures are preserved. This is how the beautiful specimens of petrified wood were formed in Arizona, where forests of conifers were buried in sands and muds rich in silica waters from ancient volcanoes. In time percolating waters dissolved the original wood but replaced its every detail by a tracery of silica which can be seen in polished pieces of these fossil logs. In other cases, the hard parts of plants or animals have been replaced by iron pyrite or calcium carbonate.

Other fossils may be molds or casts of shells and other hard parts, which have themselves been dissolved. Often the inside of a hollow snail shell will become filled with mud, which is preserved as a hard spiral internal cast, long after the shell itself has disappeared.

Other kinds of indirect evidence of prehistoric life are footprints, trails, or even burrows of animals preserved in sediments later hardened to form rock. Wastes (coprolites) of some animals and stomach stones (gastroliths) of others are occasionally found.

Impression of dinosaur skin in sandstone.

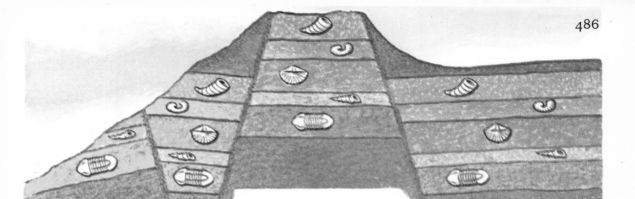

Strata containing identical fossils are of the same age even though they may occur far apart or at different depths due to earth movements.

USING FOSSILS

Fossils help solve one of the most important and common problems in geology: comparing ages of rocks in one area with those in another. Called "correlation," this is an everyday problem in petroleum and mineral exploration, mining development, surveys for dams, and construction work. Rocks of the same age can be identified by their fossils, for those deposited at the same time and under the same environmental conditions generally contain similar fossils.

Both coal and oil are formed of the remains of once-living plants and are often spoken of as fossil fuels. Carnotite, one of the most important uranium ores, is found with fossil logs in Colorado and Utah. Diatomite and some iron ores are also formed of fossil remains. In some regions fossil shells are so common they are used for lime burning or for road construction.

By studying the distribution of fossils it is also possible to reconstruct the outlines of ancient lands and seas (see maps inside front and back covers). Sometimes ancient climatic conditions and directions of ocean currents can also be determined. The study of fossil spores and pollen grains has revealed much about climatic conditions in Ice Age times and about the kinds of plants that grew then.

Fossils are the only source of information about the long history of life on earth. Those many millions of years are no less a part of history and of no less importance than the record of the past few thousand years when our history was written.

Sinclair Oil Corporation

Oil is formed by fossil plants and animals. Fossils in drill sample are the clue to oil deposits.

A scientist examines fossil-bearing sediment cores taken from the bottom of the sea.

Lamont Geophysical Laboratories

SEDIMENTARY ROCKS CONTAINING FOSSILS

Fossiliferous Limestone
(polished)
Swanton, Vermont

Sandstone with Dinosaur Footprint

Coquina Limestone
Florida

Oil Shale with Fossil Fish
Wyoming

ROCKS THAT CONTAIN FOSSILS

Virtually all fossils are found in sedimentary rocks, such as limestone and sandstone. These rocks are formed from sand, mud, and other sediments eroded from the land, or they are deposited from solutions. They are usually found in layers or strata. Sediments that make these rocks may accumulate in many different areas—in deserts, swamps, at the noses of glaciers, in lakes, in valleys along rivers, at the foot of mountains. Many are carried by wind, ice, gravity, or running water and are finally deposited in deltas, lagoons, tidal zones, or on ocean bottoms.

Sandstones are formed by the wearing away of older rocks by ice, flowing water, or wind. The fine particles—mostly quartz or silica—are cemented together when they are deposited, which is generally in shallow seas. Shales are formed of hardened clay and mud. Limestones consist mostly of calcium carbonate ($Ca\ CO_3$) which comes mainly from marine plants or animals. Often limestone rocks are made almost completely of fossil shells. Any bones, shells or other hard parts of

Layer upon layer the geology of the past is revealed in the Grand Canyon, where the Colorado River has cut down through many thicknesses of sedimentary rocks to the underlying granite.

Portion shown in photograph

limestone — Permian
sandstone
shale
sandstone and shale
limestone — Devonian Miss.
shale — Cambrian
sandstone
quartzite
shale
black schist — Pre-Cambrian
granite

Colorado River

Josef Muench

National Park Service

Fossil shells of tiny marine animals form the chalk hills and cliffs of Wind Canyon in South Dakota.

plants or animals in the sediments are transformed with them into sedimentary rocks. The chances of some animals or plants becoming fossils are much greater than others. A bird, for example, is much less likely to be a fossil than is a shellfish living in the shallow sea where sediments are deposited rapidly.

Many sedimentary rocks remain deeply buried. Others are lifted up by movements of the earth and are eroded and exposed on the land. Much of the earth's surface is covered with sedimentary rocks, and from the fossils they contain, paleontologists (scientists who study fossils) are able to piece together the story of life of the past.

Because of their origin, the other two groups of rocks—igneous and metamorphic—contain only a few fossils. Igneous rocks are formed by the cooling and hardening of molten material (magma), from deep below the surface. Metamorphic rocks, such as slate and schist, are formed by alteration of older igneous or sedimentary rocks. Often this involves intense heat or pressure.

FINDING FOSSILS

Fossils can be found in nearly all sedimentary rocks. Some fossils remain buried below the surface; others are exposed as the rock surrounding them is worn away. Good places to look for fossils are in cliffs along coasts and streams, on rocky hillsides, in quarries, along

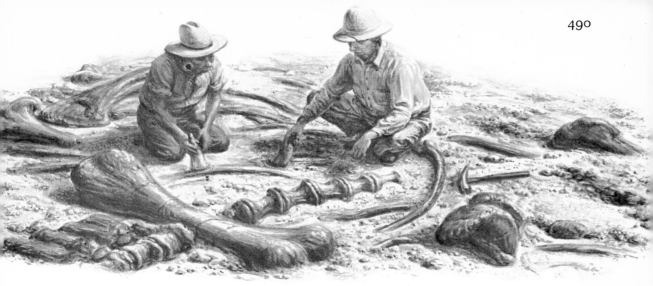

Fossils may become brittle when exposed at the surface and must be removed with great care.

ditches, railroad embankments, or road cuts —wherever there has been an excavation or erosion of the land to expose the rocks.

Marine invertebrates are by far the most common fossils and so are easiest to collect. These animals lived in conditions that aided fossilization. Some limestone rocks are composed almost entirely of fossils. Land-dwelling animals, such as birds and mammals, and also plants that grew on land are less common. Fossils of such large animals as dinosaurs are rare and are collected successfully only by expert fossil hunters.

Amateur fossil collecting does not require elaborate or expensive equipment. A hammer, a chisel, paper for wrapping and labeling, and a knapsack for carrying specimens are all that a collector needs.

In most cases it is best not to separate the fossil from the rocks in the field. This can be done at home where the rock can be broken carefully, and the fossils examined with a lens. All fossils should be labeled. Each label should identify the fossil, tell where it was collected, and give the date. It can also indicate the collector's name.

The kind of fossils found in any rock depends partly on its geologic age, and partly on the environment in which it was formed. Maps prepared by geological surveys are available for most regions. They show each kind of rock outcropping and the age of the

Plaster bandages protect large fossil bones made ready for shipment to universities and museums.

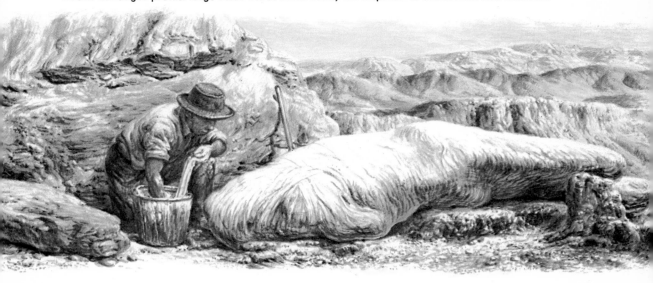

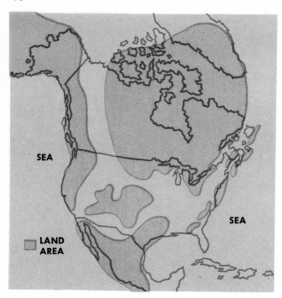

A great part of the North American continent was under water in Ordovician times, from 500 to 425 million years ago. The shallow seas were rich in invertebrates, and many of those that had shells were preserved as fossils.

rock. By studying these maps and using a fossil handbook a collector can soon learn to know the kinds of fossils that might be found in an area.

Ordovician seas covered much of eastern and midwestern United States 450 million years ago. Sand, mud, and lime were deposited. These sediments contain such marine fossils as graptolites, corals, trilobites, and brachiopods or lamp shells. Ordovician rocks are exposed in many regions and, in the United States, are abundant especially in the Cincinnati, Ohio, area where the limestone rocks are made up almost entirely of fossils. A fossil hunter in a region of Ordovician rock outcroppings would never find a dinosaur. Fossil fish (see OSTRACODERMS) have been found in Ordovician rocks in Colorado but are rare. Fossil hunting for invertebrates in Ordovician rocks would be highly rewarding, however, particularly in the Cincinnati area.

In western United States there are large areas of Mesozoic and Cenozoic sediments of continental origin in which fossils are not common. Jurassic deposits in Kansas, Montana, and Wyoming, for example, contain the remains of dinosaurs. Very few of these fossils are found, of course, and the collecting equipment needed for one of these giants far exceeds the hammer, chisel, and knapsack that are adequate for the amateur. The skull of a dinosaur, for example, may weigh half a ton. Scientists sometimes spend many months carefully removing the bones of a dinosaur. Their study of the position of the bones may give a clue as to how the animal died. Also, scientists want to find all the bones they can so that they can have as complete a skeleton as possible. Sometimes many

At the museum a skull is removed carefully from the protecting plaster and the remaining rock clinging to it (left). Large bones are supported with steel rods or frames, such as the frame being attached to the fossil dinosaur skull below.

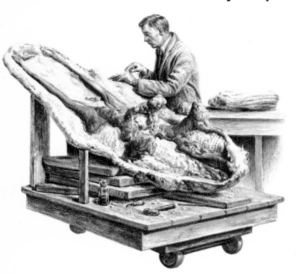

tons of rock must be moved to uncover a complete skeleton.

Bones exposed after burial for millions of years are sometimes fragile and will crumble quickly. They must be handled gently and are commonly coated with shellac and encased in plaster before being transported to a museum. At the museum the bones are reinforced, then put together to reconstruct the skeleton. If bones are missing, the scientists may be able to match them with bones in a similar skeleton or determine their probable size and shape by studying the anatomy and structure of related animals.

When the skeleton is finally put together in a lifelike pose, scientists can use it for study purposes, and people who visit the museum can see what the prehistoric reptile looked like. Sometimes the animal is fully restored from the skeletal remains, giving it the form and appearance the experts believe the animal had. Some of this must be done by guessing, but most restorations are based on knowledge of conditions and anatomy. Bits of skin impressions in sand have been discovered and also nests of dinosaur eggs. All this information is used by the scientists in deducing what these animals looked like and how they moved and acted in life. The habitat scenes of dinosaurs and other animals and plant life in these books are artists' concepts, based on facts which fossils themselves have disclosed about life of the past.

In contrast to such giant fossils as dinosaurs are microfossils. These are the microscopic remains of whole plants and animals or of their parts, such as the scales of fishes. Microfossils are rarely collected by amateurs, but they are of great interest and importance to scientists. Hundreds of perfect specimens may be found in one small sample. Microfossils are especially useful in correlating rock strata (see page 486).

Teams of scientists sometimes work many months in assembling a fossil skeleton in a lifelike pose. Missing bones are replaced with bones made of plaster or plastic. When the scaffolds are removed, the skeleton stands alone. Its unconnected bones are supported by metal rods that are scarcely visible.

PITCHBLENDE
(uranium ore)
Saxony

FOSSILS AND TIME

Calendars of geologic time allow us to date such events as the rise of a mountain range or the occurrence of certain fossil groups. This system gives only relative age. Geologists speak of a fossil as late Cambrian, meaning it was found in rocks about 550 million years old. Or an early Cretaceous dinosaur is one that lived about 100 million years ago.

Most early attempts to measure ages of rocks or the age of the earth were largely guesswork. As early as 450 B.C., however,

Herodotus suggested that the rate at which sediment was deposited indicated that thousands of years had been necessary to build the broad delta at the mouth of the Nile.

Various estimates of the age of the earth were made during the 1800's. These were based on the total thickness of sedimentary rocks and the salt content of the oceans. A maximum age of about 100 million years was arrived at by these methods, but the many corrections in these calculations all tended to increase the earth's age greatly. It was the discovery of radioactivity in 1896 that provided a basis for a reliable geological clock.

Uranium and other radioactive minerals, although they occur in small amounts, are widely distributed in igneous rocks. All have unstable atomic nuclei and continuously break down into other, more stable elements. Uranium, for example, slowly breaks down into lead and helium. This process is totally independent of all known physical and chemical changes in the environment. Although the rate of breakdown or disintegration is very slow, it can be measured accurately. Measurements show that 1 gram of uranium of one type disintegrates into 1/7,600 grams of lead every million years. Therefore, the age of a rock can be determined by the ratio of lead to uranium still in it. Other radioactive elements, such as rubidium-strontium, potassium-argon, and carbon isotopes, are also used in this manner to measure geologic time. Carbon 14 disintegrates more rapidly.

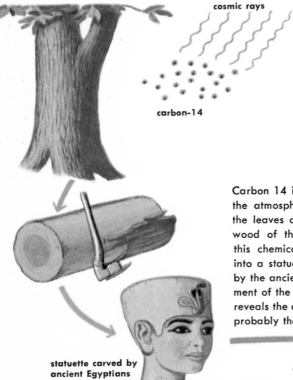

cosmic rays

carbon-14

statuette carved by
ancient Egyptians

fragment of statuette
found in pyramid

Carbon 14 in carbon dioxide from the atmosphere was absorbed by the leaves of a growing tree. The wood of the tree which includes this chemical isotope was carved into a statuette and left in a tomb by the ancient Egyptians. Measurement of the carbon 14 in the wood reveals the age of the statuette and probably the age of the tomb.

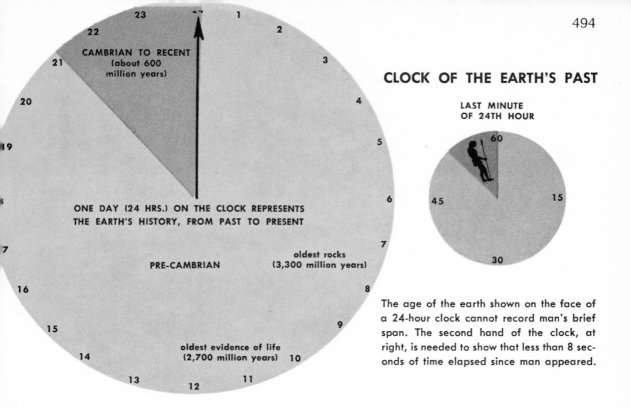

CLOCK OF THE EARTH'S PAST

LAST MINUTE
OF 24TH HOUR

ONE DAY (24 HRS.) ON THE CLOCK REPRESENTS
THE EARTH'S HISTORY, FROM PAST TO PRESENT

CAMBRIAN TO RECENT
(about 600
million years)

PRE-CAMBRIAN

oldest rocks
(3,300 million years)

oldest evidence of life
(2,700 million years)

The age of the earth shown on the face of a 24-hour clock cannot record man's brief span. The second hand of the clock, at right, is needed to show that less than 8 seconds of time elapsed since man appeared.

Half of any given quantity will disintegrate in 5,568 years. For this reason it is most useful in dating younger objects, such as prehistoric pieces of wood, charcoal, or cloth. By these methods an accurate geological time scale can be constructed.

We now know that the oldest widespread common fossils—those of lower Cambrian age—are about 600 million years old. The oldest fossils (probably algae found in Rhodesia) appear to be more than 2,700 million years old. The oldest rocks so far discovered come from Rhodesia, Wyoming, and Manitoba and are about 3,300 million years old. These rocks do not represent the total age of the earth, however. The earth's age is more difficult to determine but is believed to be 4,500 to 5,000 million years. This age has been determined by measuring the rate of expansion of the universe and present distances from the earth of various outlying galaxies and by studies of rocks and meteorites or shooting stars.

Such vast periods of time are difficult to understand. Suppose an imaginary tree planted at the time of the earth's origin has since grown continuously at the microscopic rate of 1/10,000 of an inch every year. At that slow rate the tree would now be about eight miles high. A tree planted at the dawn of Cambrian time would be about a mile high. A tree planted when man first appeared would be two feet tall, and one planted at the time of Christ would be 1/5 of an inch tall.

Or suppose we show the history of the earth on the face of a 24-hour clock. If 5,000 million years is used as the probable age of the earth, each minute represents 3,470,000 years. Pre-Cambrian time would take up 21 hours of the 24. The oldest known rocks were formed between 7 and 8 o'clock, though it is assumed that older ones lie below them. Primitive forms of life appear between 10 and 11 o'clock, about 2,700 million years ago. Man appears in the last 7 or 8 seconds before the hour of midnight. All of recorded history is compressed into one-half of one second, just one tick of the clock of earth's long history. (See LIFE'S ORIGIN AND DEVELOPMENT.)

These tremendous periods of time are of great importance to us in understanding the significance of fossils. Only by appreciating this time scale can we recognize the nature of the far-reaching changes that have taken place in the life of the earth.

FOUR-O'CLOCK
Mirabilis froebeli
wild

MARVEL OF PERU
Mirabilis jalapa
cultivated

FOUR-O'CLOCKS are tall, square-stemmed plants with large, heart-shaped leaves. Half a dozen species grow wild in North America, mostly on dry wastelands of the plains. They spread rapidly and become weeds. Their flowers lack petals, but the calyx forms a white to reddish trumpet.

The common cultivated Four-o'clock (*Mirabilis jalapa*) is a member of the same genus, which includes some 250 species most abundant in the tropics. Also called Marvel-of-Peru, this favorite of the past grows three feet tall and bears two-inch fragrant trumpets which open late in the afternoon and remain open until it is fully light in the morning. In temperate regions, the Four-o'clock is grown from seed as an annual. In its warm native land, however, it is a perennial and develops a fleshy root that may weigh 40 pounds. Some gardeners dig the roots every fall and reset them in the spring. Bougainvillea is also a member of this family (see BOUGAINVILLEA).

FOXES are all about the same size and are all members of the dog family. All foxes feed on small mammals and birds, occasionally on fruits and insects. They hunt at night and usually dig burrows in which they rear their young, commonly four to a litter. When contracted, the pupil of a fox's eye is elliptical, like a cat's, rather than round as in domestic dogs and wolves. Foxes, unlike dogs, are mainly nocturnal in habits, although they sometimes hunt during the day when they are pressed to find food, as for a litter of pups in the early spring.

The Red Fox (*Vulpes fulva*), found in northern Europe, Asia, and North America, lives in brushland or along the forest edges. Several color forms occur: black, silver (hairs black with white tips), and "cross" (a reddish pelt striped with black). All these can be found in a single litter of young, though red is the normal color. "Silver fox" was a very popular fur for many years, and since this color phase is not common in nature, "silvers" were bred on fur farms. The Red Fox is noted for its cunning and has been hunted for sport for hundreds of years: by horse and hound, tracking in the snow, trapping, and other

The Red Fox is known for its cunning in eluding hunters and their dogs. Though heavily hunted, it has become more abundant in rural areas of the United States.
Roy Pinney

CROSS FOX

BLACK FOX

SILVER FOX

GRAY FOX

Cross, Silver, and Black Foxes are color phases of the Red Fox. The Gray Fox is a separate species.

methods. These foxes eat mostly mice, but they may become pests by making raids on poultry, particularly when they have pups to feed. Males usually stay with their mates and assist in feeding and rearing the young, which are born blind and helpless. In temperate climates, the young are born in the spring and are ready to leave the family by autumn. They are mature by the following spring.

The Gray Fox (*Urocyon cinereoargenteus*) is common throughout most of the United States southward into northern South America. In eastern United States it lives in wooded areas and occasionally climbs trees. In western United States it lives in more open country and digs its den in sandy banks. The Gray Fox has a black-tipped tail; all color phases of the Red Fox have white-tipped tails.

The Arctic Fox (*Alopex lagopus*) lives in the northern tundra where it feeds on ground squirrels, lemmings, hares, and many birds. Sometimes it eats fish, dead seals, or dead whales. The Arctic Fox may be white or "blue," which is really bluish-gray or bluish-brown. It burrows in the snow to make a temporary den for rearing its young. Arctic travelers often hear this fox's high-pitched barks and yelps.

The Kit Fox (*Vulpes macrotis*), a small, big-eared member of the fox group, lives in the deserts of southwestern United States and also in Mexico. Exceedingly shy and a fast runner, the Kit Fox can endure extreme desert heat and needs little water. The Swift Fox (*Vulpes velox*), which has short ears, is closely related to the Kit Fox. Years ago the Swift Fox was abundant on the prairies of central United States and southern Canada and was commonly found with the great herds of Bison. Now it is rare. The Fennec Fox (*Fennecus zerda*), also much like the Kit Fox in appearance, has exceptionally long ears, is small in size, and has a bushy tail. It lives in the deserts of northern Africa.

ARCTIC FOX

FENNEC FOX

KIT FOX

This Great Frigate-bird will chase the Brown Booby until it drops its fish, which the marauder will then grab.

GREAT FRIGATE-BIRD—40 in.
Fregata minor
Coasts of tropical oceans

BROWN BOOBY—30 in.
Sula leucogaster
Coasts of tropical oceans

FRIGATE-BIRDS are skilled flyers. Sea birds of the tropics, they stay in the air most of the time. Frigate-birds' legs are so short and their wings so long, it is difficult for them to rise from land and nearly impossible for them to take off from the sea. When they alight, it is always on a tree, buoy, or similar elevation. They capture fish by swooping or hovering just over the water or by stealing from gulls, pelicans, or other sea birds. During courtship and nest building, male birds inflate their orange throat pouches, which then turn red, and keep them puffed up for hours. Females lay a single egg in the frail nest built by the male. The newly hatched chicks are covered with thick, white down. This beauty lasts only a short time, and the moment their long wings begin to grow, they become awkward, droopy creatures.

MAGNIFICENT FRIGATE-BIRD—40 in.
Fregata magnificens
Tropical Atlantic and Western Pacific

male

young b

nestling

FROGS and Toads are amphibians that do not have tails when mature. They are called anurans, which in Greek means "without a tail." Most toads have rough skin; frogs generally have smooth skin.

Frogs and toads are abundant in almost all moist, warm habitats throughout the world. They cannot live in salt or brackish waters. A few kinds spend their entire lives in water, but most come out onto the land frequently and often for long periods. In semiarid regions toads and frogs are found near whatever water is available or in burrows from which they emerge only at night.

No other backboned animals have the unusual body form or strange method of movement that marks frogs and toads. Their long and powerful hind legs, used for jumping, are much larger than their front legs, which

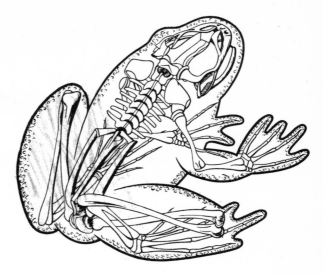

Skeleton of frog shows the long bones in its powerful hind legs and the large pelvic girdle which receives the shock of the landing. Note the small number of vertebrae in the backbones with stout riblike projections and the skull which joins the backbone without a neck.

catch the weight of their body when they land. In kinds that crawl rather than jump, such as the European Green Toad, both pairs of legs are the same size.

Other body changes also help absorb the shocks of leaping and landing. For example, the pelvic girdle, which receives the jolt of the hind legs in the leap, is greatly enlarged. It extends forward almost half the length of the body. The tail bones are fused into a solid shock-absorbing bar, which lies in the middle of the pelvic girdle. There are only six to ten free bones in the backbone, the smallest number in all vertebrates. The chest region is encased in a greatly enlarged pectoral girdle. Frogs and toads have stout projections on each side of the vertebrae but no ribs, which would break easily in landings.

Completely aquatic frogs and toads have small eyes and have also lost their eyelids. But most frogs and toads have large eyes and have not only eyelids but also transparent rims on their large lower lids. They can look out through these thin membranes even when their lids are closed.

Frogs and toads feed mostly on worms, insects, spiders, and other small animals. Occasionally they eat small mammals or birds.

female

FAMILY TREE OF FROGS AND TOADS

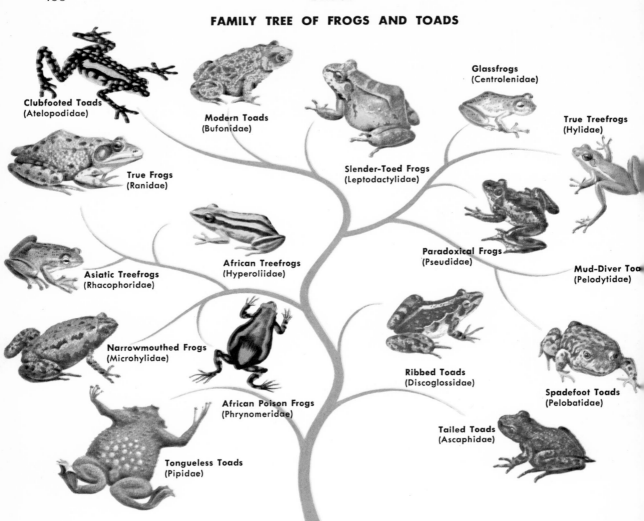

Clubfooted Toads
(Atelopodidae)

Modern Toads
(Bufonidae)

Glassfrogs
(Centrolenidae)

True Treefrogs
(Hylidae)

True Frogs
(Ranidae)

Slender-Toed Frogs
(Leptodactylidae)

Asiatic Treefrogs
(Rhacophoridae)

African Treefrogs
(Hyperoliidae)

Paradoxical Frogs
(Pseudidae)

Mud-Diver Toa
(Pelodytidae)

Narrowmouthed Frogs
(Microhylidae)

Ribbed Toads
(Discoglossidae)

Spadefoot Toads
(Pelobatidae)

African Poison Frogs
(Phrynomeridae)

Tailed Toads
(Ascaphidae)

Tongueless Toads
(Pipidae)

Most kinds react only to moving objects, which they catch by flipping out their sticky tongue. In most kinds, the tongue is attached at the front of the mouth, allowing the greatest possible reach. Some aquatic frogs and toads have no tongue, and in others the tongue is attached at the rear of the mouth.

Frogs and toads, like other carnivorous animals, have relatively short intestines, less than twice the length of their body. Vegetarian animals have much longer intestines.

Frogs and toads, both the adults and the tadpoles, are eaten by wading birds, small mammals, snakes, and fishes. Frog legs are considered delicacies, and frogs are also used as laboratory animals.

Frogs and toads usually breed in warm, wet weather in spring. Those that live in dry regions breed whenever the rains come. This may be in summer or fall. When no heavy rains fall, they may even skip a season. Those that live in water begin breeding as soon as the temperature of the water is warm enough.

At the proper time the males seek the nearest water of suitable depth, then inflate their throat pouches with air and start "calling" by forcing the air out over their vocal cords. Each kind of frog or toad has a distinctive call, which directs females and other males to the breeding site. A chorus of males calling at a breeding spot may be almost deafening to anyone nearby. Each male clasps in his forelegs the first female that comes within reach. Then, as the eggs are laid a few at a time, he squirts over them a small jet of sperm-bearing fluid.

All female frogs and toads produce two streams of eggs, one from each ovary, but in only a few types do these remain as two distinct strings after they are laid. In most kinds they form a mass under the water or a film on the surface. Some frogs lay their eggs on moist land.

Each egg hatches into a larva, or "tadpole." The larva has adhesive organs, one on each side below its mouth, for attaching to underwater objects. It also has large external gills just behind its head. The external gills soon disappear and are replaced by internal gills, similar to those of fishes. Water drawn into the mouth passes into the gill chamber and emerges from one or two small openings located on the tadpole's side or, in some cases, on its belly.

Tadpoles feed on algae and other small plants which grow on underwater surfaces. Their "scrapers" are tiny projections on the flexible disc around their small, horny jaws. Unlike their flesh-eating parents, tadpoles have long, coiled intestines.

When a tadpole starts to "transform" into the froglet (imago) stage, its mouth disc disappears and its jaws lose their horny rims. Hind legs appear at the base of its tail, which then shortens. Eventually front legs appear. Small changes in the pattern and texture of the skin also occur before the froglet becomes a completely tail-less adult.

Frogs of the family Ranidae are the most common ground-dwelling frogs of Europe and North America, but some members of the

Frogs and toads catch their insect prey by means of their sticky tongue, which can be flipped out quickly.

family are tree frogs and others are narrow-mouthed, baggy-bodied burrowers.

Members of the genus *Rana* are found everywhere in the world except in salt water or in cold regions. The largest anuran in the world, the Goliath Frog of Africa, belongs to this genus. Common North American species are the Bullfrog (*Rana catesbeiana*), Greenfrog (*Rana clamitans*), and the Grassfrog or Pickerel Frog (*Rana palustris*), and Leopard Frog (*Rana pipiens*). Some species are believed to be somewhat resistant to salt water. They feed on crabs, which they kill by hugging tightly in their forelegs. Then they crack the shells with their bare thumb bones, which are sharp, clawlike and dangerous to humans.

Only one frog in North America, the Bullfrog, is generally considered edible, and only its large hind legs are eaten. Normally it takes about five years for a Bullfrog to attain edible size. The market is supplied by professional frog hunters, who dazzle the frogs with lights and then net or spear them.

Frogs lay their eggs in a jellylike mass. Each fertilized egg develops an embryo. After a period of time, a tadpole hatches from each egg and clings to vegetation by adhesive suckers under its mouth. At first the tadpole has branched, outer gills, but soon these gills are grown over by skin. After a period of growth, the hind legs appear, then the front legs. At this stage the tadpole looks like an adult frog, although it still has a stubby tail when it emerges on land. Soon the tail is absorbed.

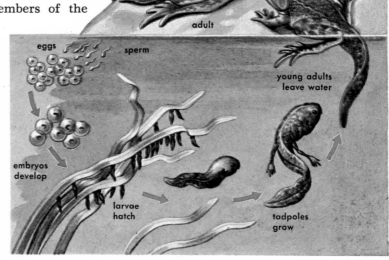

adult

eggs
sperm
young adults leave water
embryos develop
larvae hatch
tadpoles grow

Roy Pinney

Leopard Frogs have three or four different calls, each communicating a specific meaning to other frogs.

The Hairy Frog (*Trichobatrachus*) of the French Cameroons is an unusual African species. Adult males have long, hairlike strands of skin on their hind legs and the rear sides of their body. The function of these strands, absent in females and also in young males, is not known, but they are believed to be useful in respiration. Mature male African tickle frogs (*Arthroleptis*) have very long third fingers; females do not. When annoyed, a fat-bodied, narrow-headed African frog (*Hemisus*) puffs up its body and arches its back, then stretches its legs and bends down its

GOLIATH FROG—body 10 in. long
Rana goliath
African Congo, largest of the frogs

RICORD ROBBER FROG—0.6 to 1.2 in.
Eleutherodactylus ricordi
Florida; smallest North American frog

head in a menacing manner. Another member of this genus carries its eggs in a pouch on its belly, and the tadpoles do not emerge until they are well developed. Still another lays eggs in a depression in the ground, digging an escape tunnel to a nearby source of water for the newly hatched larvae.

Poison Frogs (*Dendrobates*), found in Central and South America, have a very powerful skin poison which is used by natives on the tips of their darts and arrows. The poison will kill large animals almost instantly. These frogs lay their eggs in small pools of water in hollow trees or logs, where the larvae also develop. The tadpoles have strong mouth discs with which they attach themselves to adults that hop into the pools. They release themselves when the frog hops into the water again, traveling in this piggyback fashion from pool to pool.

Rhacophorids (*Rhacophorus* spp.) are a large group of frogs that have expanded tips on their fingers and toes. Found in southern Asia and on the large islands of the East Indies, these frogs usually live in trees and lay their eggs on the leaves a few feet above water. They beat the gelatin surrounding the eggs into a frothy mass with their hind legs. In a short time the eggs hatch, and the larvae drop into the water where they complete their development to become air-breathing adults.

Some species lay their eggs on land just above the water level of a stream or a pond. They also beat their eggs into a froth, and the larvae develop in the froth until rains raise the level of the water and they can swim free. Sometimes these frogs make mistakes and lay their eggs too late, too soon, too far from water, or in a place where they are exposed to the sun.

Some rhacophorids have large, fully webbed feet and hands. When they leap, they spread these webs and sail long distances.

About one hundred species of African frogs belong to the family Hyperoliidae. Like the rhacophorids, they have widened tips on their fingers and toes for climbing trees. These are among the most beautifully marked frogs in the world. Some lay their eggs on leaves in

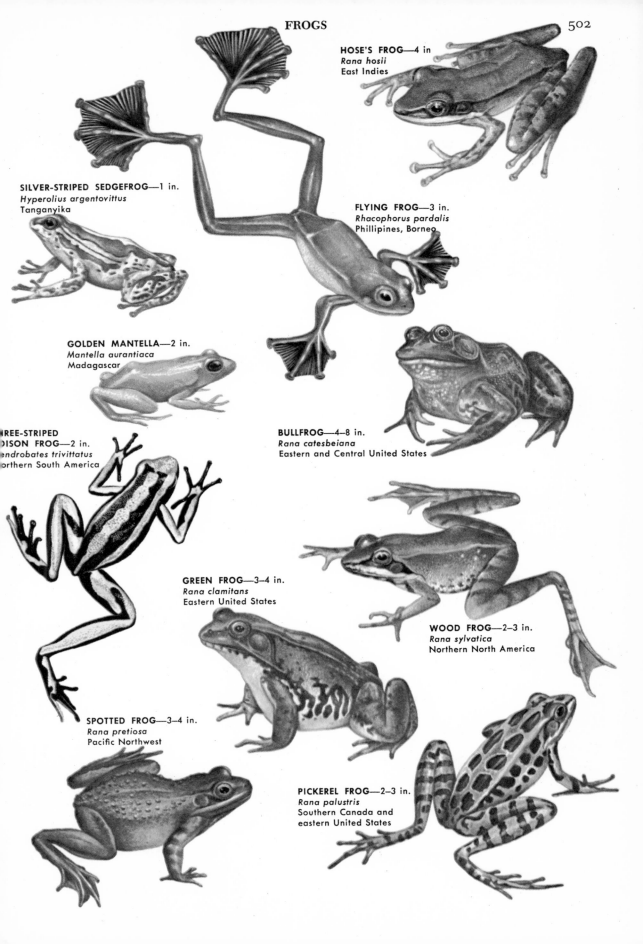

HOSE'S FROG—4 in
Rana hosii
East Indies

SILVER-STRIPED SEDGEFROG—1 in.
Hyperolius argentovittus
Tanganyika

FLYING FROG—3 in.
Rhacophorus pardalis
Phillipines, Borneo

GOLDEN MANTELLA—2 in.
Mantella aurantiaca
Madagascar

**THREE-STRIPED
POISON FROG—2 in.**
Dendrobates trivittatus
Northern South America

BULLFROG—4–8 in.
Rana catesbeiana
Eastern and Central United States

GREEN FROG—3–4 in.
Rana clamitans
Eastern United States

WOOD FROG—2–3 in.
Rana sylvatica
Northern North America

SPOTTED FROG—3–4 in.
Rana pretiosa
Pacific Northwest

PICKEREL FROG—2–3 in.
Rana palustris
Southern Canada and
eastern United States

trees, but most kinds lay their eggs in water or on land at the water's edge. The female of one kind (*Leptopelis*) holds her eggs in her mouth until the froglets are ready to emerge. During this time, of course, she does not eat. When disturbed, some frogs of this genus "play 'possum" by opening their mouth and putting their hands over their head. (See AMPHIBIANS; TOADS; TREE FROGS; and consult index for listing of frogs and toads described separately in these volumes.)

Mutants or Sports

FRUIT FLY—normal   beaded wings   vestigial wings
Drosophila melanogaster
0.2 in.

ORNATE CHORUS FROG—1 in.
Pseudacris ornata
Eastern North America

PANAMANIAN POISON
FROG—1 in.
Dendrobates auratus
Central America

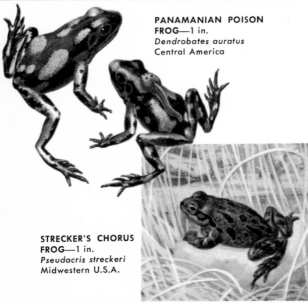

STRECKER'S CHORUS
FROG—1 in.
Pseudacris streckeri
Midwestern U.S.A.

FRUIT FLIES (Trypetidae) are among the most destructive pests of fruits. Most species are small to medium in size and have banded wings. Their eggs, usually deposited under the skin of the fruit, may require only a few days or as long as three weeks to hatch. The larvae or maggots burrow through the pulp as they feed and are full grown in from ten days to six weeks. Then they drop to the ground to pupate.

The Mediterranean Fruit Fly attacks oranges, grapefruit, peaches, pears, and many other kinds of fruits. It is found in nearly all subtropical countries and was successfully eradicated when it appeared in Florida in 1929. It was eliminated a second time in 1956 and today is not known to occur in the United States. Apple Maggots and Cherry Fruit Flies are northern insects that also attack pears, plums, blueberries, and blackberries. Goldenrod Gall Flies cause the formation of galls on goldenrod.

Members of another family (Drosophilidae) are also known as fruit flies. Their larvae feed in decaying fruit and in fungi. One widespread species (*Drosophila melanogaster*) is commonly used in studies of heredity because it is easily reared and completes its entire life cycle in about 10 days.

GOPHER FROG—2½–4½ in.
Rana areolata
Southern U.S.

RED-LEGGED
FROG—2–5 in.
Rana aurora
Pacific Coast of United States

RED-LEGGED FROG

FRUITS. A seed is the fertilized, ripened ovary of a flower. The fruit consists of the seed and various other parts of the flower which surround and protect the seed until it sprouts and starts a new plant. Some fruits are fleshy, juicy, colorful, and conspicuous. Others are small, hard, and dry. Some kinds are so small they escape notice. Giant Sequoia seeds, for example, are very small. It may take as many as 3,000 to weigh an ounce, yet they can grow to be the largest of all living things. (See SEEDS; VEGETABLES.)

FUCHSIAS (*Fuchsia* spp.) were discovered in South America nearly three centuries ago. They were named for a German botanist whose name was Fuchs—which, incidentally, means fox.

Fuchsias have had several up-and-down periods of popularity. At present they are riding high in public favor. So many new varieties are being produced by plant breeders that people have trouble telling them apart. From two or three species about 2,000 varieties have been developed. More than 75 species grow wild in tropical South America.

Some of the dainty blossoms remind one of a ballerina with flaring points on her skirt, and one of the varieties has been named Ballerina. Also, because of their hanging or pendant position, they suggest large colored ornaments, such as might be used to decorate a lady's ear and are sometimes called Lady's Eardrops. A few species have erect flowers.

Growing the plants is so easy and interesting that many people take it up as a hobby and try to develop a collection of the choicest varieties. One indication of the interest in fuchsias is that as long ago as 1923 the American Fuchsia Society was organized.

Colors of fuchsias now include almost any combination of whites, reds, blues, and purples. Besides developing new shades or combinations of colors, plant breeders have produced new kinds that can endure direct sunlight. Formerly only those with orange or red color could be grown in the sun. One kind with small flowers can stand cold weather but is grown indoors, except in western U.S.

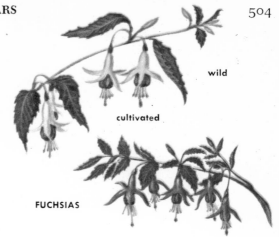

FUCHSIAS

Fuchsias prefer cool, moist, shady conditions. Many are seen in mild coastal areas, as in California. Some are trained in tree shape, some are rather viny and look especially pretty in hanging baskets, and many grow into bush form.

FULMARS are tube-nosed swimming birds of the Arctic and North Atlantic oceans. They follow whaling ships and sealers and eat the waste thrown overboard. They land only to nest in large colonies on sea cliffs. Females lay one egg on a bare ledge. When annoyed or alarmed, nesting Fulmars squirt a stream of oil at whatever disturbs them. The young are fed by regurgitation.

Fulmars soar whenever possible but are strong fliers.

Fulmar incubating eggs

FULMAR—18 in.
Fulmarus glacialis
Arctic, northern Atlantic
and Pacific oceans

SPORE GROWTH—HIGHLY MAGNIFIED

spore

hypha beginning
to grow

hyphae

mycelium

fruiting body

A fungus spore first grows a single thread, or hypha. Many of these threads form the mycelium. In time, spore-producing or fruiting bodies develop from the mycelium. Mushrooms are the fruiting bodies of a large and extensive mycelium that grows underground or in rotted wood.

FUNGI are plants that contain no chlorophyll. Almost all non-flowering plants belong in this group. Since fungi cannot manufacture their own food, they must obtain it already made. In this respect they resemble animals. Those that feed on other living organisms are called parasites; those that feed on dead remains are called saprophytes.

Fungi are divided into several classes. The simplest are the bacteria. Bacteria are one-celled plants, although the individual cells may grow together in long chains or irregular masses. They reproduce by fission—merely splitting into two cells.

Slime molds, another group of fungi, differ from all other plants in having no cell walls (except around their spores). Most scientists classify slime molds as plants, but others believe they are a type of colonial amoeba.

Nearly all true fungi—all except the bacteria and slime molds—have bodies made up of a mass of threadlike filaments. Each thread is called a hypha, and the entire mass of threads is called a mycelium.

True fungi produce spores. These very small reproductive bodies are much like seeds. Usually carried by the winds, they germinate and form new plants when they land in a place with sufficient moisture and food. Spores are formed in little cases called sporangia, as in Bread Mold, or break off in succession from the ends of hyphae, as in Green Mold. Many fungi produce complex fruiting

bodies which are large enough to see. Examples are mushrooms, pore fungi, puffballs, gill and cup fungi. These fruiting bodies contain spores, produced either in a saclike structure called an ascus or on a clublike cell called the basidium.

Lichens consist of two kinds of plants—a fungus and an alga. A relationship of this sort in which each seems to need the other in order to survive is called symbiosis.

Fungi are found almost everywhere—in the air, soil, or water. Everything you touch has bacteria or true fungi on it, usually in the form of spores so small that you cannot see them. Spores have been collected on glass slides exposed to the air six miles above the earth. They have also been collected from ships in the middle of the ocean. Fungi grow

Maytag Dairy Farms

BLUE CHEESE
flavored by a mold

in the tropics and also in arctic regions. Often there are billions of bacteria and true fungi in a square foot of good soil. Bacteria grow in the bodies of all animals, including man. Most kinds are harmless, but some cause disease. Many scientists believe that bacteria were the first true living organisms.

The more than 100,000 kinds of fungi—almost a third of all the kinds of plants known—are an important group. Their greatest value is the part they play in maintaining the balance of nature. Fungi are responsible for the decay of all plant and animal remains.

Fungi or their products are used practically every day. Bread is baked with yeast, a fungus that causes the bread to rise and be fluffy and soft. Blue cheeses, such as Roquefort, get their consistency, flavor, and color from blue and green molds. The souring of milk is caused by bacteria, and the flavor of butter is also due to bacteria.

All alcoholic beverages are fermented by yeast. Among the organic acids produced by fungi are gallic acid used in dyes, citric acid used in soft drinks and medicines, gluconic acid used in medicines, and acetic acid used in chemistry. Vinegar is a weak solution of acetic acid produced from fruit juices by certain bacteria. Fungi are used to tan leather and are the source of some vitamins.

Fungi produce antibiotics such as penicillin and streptomycin, the so-called miracle drugs. Yeast is effective in treating acne, and puffball spores are sometimes used by veterinarians to stop bleeding.

Air consists of about 20 percent oxygen and 80 per cent nitrogen. All animals and almost all plants are unable to use the nitrogen in the air even though nitrogen is an important part of protoplasm, proteins, vitamins, and many other organic compounds. Certain bacteria—some free-living and others associated with roots of legumes, such as beans, clover, and alfalfa—can convert the free nitrogen of the air into compounds that higher plants and animals can use.

Fungi associated with the roots of many plants, particularly trees, form a symbiotic relationship called mycorrhiza. The fungi get their food from the roots, and the roots in turn are able to absorb more water and minerals by the aid of the fungus.

Fungi are also harmful to man's interest. Cloth, fruits, and vegetables are quickly rotted by fungi. Decay of lumber and wooden buildings is caused by fungi, mostly belonging to the pore fungus group. These fungi can soon destroy sidings, sills, or floors. To prevent this from happening, building timbers are well dried. Any pieces that might contact the soil or any moisture are treated with a preservative that keeps the fungus from growing.

Fungi also cause diseases. Diphtheria, typhoid, tuberculosis, lockjaw, and some types of pneumonia are caused by bacteria. Certain yeasts cause skin diseases of man. Other bacteria cause plant diseases, such as crown gall, bacterial rot of orchids, and fire blight of apples and pears. Wheat rust, apple scab, carnation wilt, mango anthracnose, and withertip of citrus are a few of thousands of plant diseases caused by fungi. A watermold causes late blight of potatoes and tomatoes.

True fungi also cause athlete's foot, ringworm, and many internal diseases of humans. Spores of fungi produce allergies, causing hay-fever type breathing difficulties. Some people sneeze violently when entering a room where there are molds or mildews.

Many kinds of fungi are edible, but some are poisonous and may cause death. "Toadstool" is a name commonly used for poisonous mushrooms. Certain bacteria cause food poisoning, particularly when the food is left unrefrigerated in hot weather. Fish and poultry spoil especially quickly. (See index for fungi described separately in these volumes.)

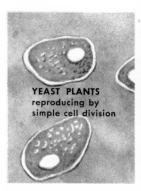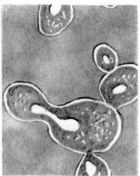

YEAST PLANTS reproducing by simple cell division

FUR FARMING. Much of North America was first explored by trappers after fur. Animals sometimes were kept alive until their pelts were prime, but in the early days there was no breeding or raising of animals for their furs.

In the late 1800's experiments in raising Silver Foxes were conducted on Prince Edward Island in Canada. The Silver Fox, which has black fur with white interspersed and a white-tipped tail, is a sport or mutation of the Red Fox. The first of these furs were sold in 1918 and brought as much as $2,600 apiece. Soon people paid large sums to get pairs of these foxes in the belief they had found a way to become wealthy overnight.

In 1935, Platinum Foxes, another variation of the Red Fox, were imported from Norway. Some of these furs sold for $13,000 per pelt. Fox farming is now carried on largely in the northern tier of states and Canada where the cold climate seems best suited for producing prime pelts.

Chinchillas had a similar beginning in the United States. Breeding pairs sold for

Malak-Annan Photo Features

Fur farms provide a growing percentage of the annual harvest of furs. These are Silver Foxes being raised on a fur farm on Prince Edward Island, Canada.

This buff-colored mink is a special color phase bred by a rancher. The normal color of a wild mink is a deep chestnut-brown.

Hansche Bros. of Spring Lake Mink Farm

large sums of money. People who bought the animals knew little about how to care for them. Worse, they found that the only market for the animals was other people who wanted to raise them. (See CHINCHILLAS.)

Mink farms are the most abundant and most profitable of the fur farms today. A number of color variations from the natural brown pelt have been developed on mink ranches. The first of these was the Silverblu, and now there are several popular shades of blue in addition to light brown and white.

Mink do best in separate cages which are about 6 feet long, 18 inches wide, and 2 feet high. These are generally set off the ground so that droppings fall through and the cages are kept reasonably clean. The mink's diet should be about three-fourths meat, a part of which may be fish. While mink pelts do not bring the fabulous prices that early fox farmers got for skins, they average out well so that mink ranches are a good business. Totally, the wholesale value of mink pelts produced annually in the United States is about $200 million.

Nutrias or Coypus are rather new to the fur trade. They are water-dwelling rodents that were introduced from South America. A Nutria's most valuable fur is on its belly. This is especially true of females, for the fur on their backs is not only coarse but also unusable because the mammary glands are located so high on the sides. This unusual location permits the young to suckle while the mother is swimming. Nutrias are vegetarians and feeding them is not expensive. There is almost no market for their fur, however. In Louisiana, animals that escaped to the wild a few years ago have multiplied rapidly and are pests in some areas. Pelts from these wild animals more than supply the market needs.

Fur farming has many advantages over trapping. Wild animals may damage their fur in fighting or in struggling to get free when trapped. Animals raised in pens rarely have damaged fur, and their fur can be harvested when it is at its prime. Also the fur farmer can use his knowledge of genetics to produce variations, thus stimulating sales.

A fur farmer has problems, however. He must provide individual cages or pens for each of his animals and must see that they breed in season. Diseases can become epidemics. Digestive disorders from spoiled food can spread quickly and kill many animals in only a day or two.

An animal's pelt is harvested when it is at its best or prime (usually in winter). The method used to kill the animal is as painless as possible and must also preserve the fur. Most small animals are killed by using anesthetics or gas. Fox pelts are often taken by injecting the animals with a fatal dose of a poison, such as strychnine. The animals are skinned and their pelts, the flesh scraped free, pulled tight (but not stretched) over a shaped board or wire frame. They are cured in a dry, cool place. When dry they are bundled ready for sale. Most furs are sold at auctions, and the larger ones in North America are in New York, Denver, Montreal, and Winnipeg. Unlike auction sales of other merchandise, a fur buyer may set a minimum price on his furs or bid the price up himself.

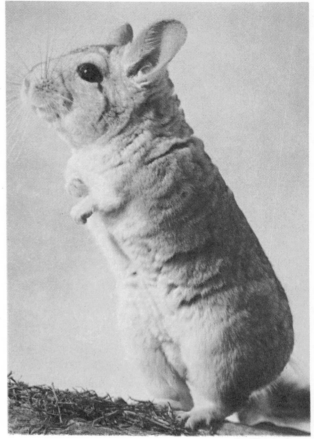

Roy Pinney

Chinchillas are the smallest animals raised for their fur, and the few coats made from their pelts have sold for the highest prices.

South American Nutrias or Coypus are easy to raise on fur farms, but their fur brings a low price. Nutrias have escaped captivity in some areas and become pests.

GABBRO is a coarse-grained igneous rock similar to diorite but darker. The same minerals are present, but in gabbro there is more iron and magnesium and less light-colored plagioclase. Gabbro is found in thick sills, dikes, and lopoliths. Gabbro lopoliths occur in the Bushveld region of South Africa; near Sudbury, Canada; and at Duluth, Minnesota, where blotches and veins of "red rock" show, due to a concentration of red feldspar.

COARSE GABBRO
a common, dark
igneous rock
Salem, Mass.

GAILLARDIAS (*Gaillardia* spp.), though named after a Frenchman, are actually native American flowers. Two important species grow wild on the plains and prairies all the way from Mexico to western Canada.

From the wild gaillardias many attractive garden varieties have been developed. These are grown from seeds or cuttings. Their gay blossoms of yellow, orange, and red brighten gardens for months until frost kills them.

Gaillardias are composites, with large, attractive daisy-like flowers. Their broad, petal-like rays are notched with a V at the end. The flower's central disk is purple. Some of the cultivated forms have double flowers, and some look like small pincushions.

GALAXY. The stars are all around us. Some are bright and nearby, but larger and larger telescopes reveal fainter and more distant stars until it seems as if there were no end to them. Nevertheless, the system of stars that we live in does have a limited size, even though it is very large. Such a system is called a galaxy, and our own galaxy is called the Milky Way (see MILKY WAY), after the faint band of light that circles the sky. The Milky Way contains 100 billion stars of which our sun is just one.

The Milky Way is a type of galaxy called spiral, which consists of three parts: the disc, the spiral arms, and the halo. Most of the stars are scattered through the region of the disc, which bulges at the center and tapers down at the edges. Embedded in the disc are the spiral arms that wind out from its center. Often there are two arms opposite each other, but some galaxies have many arms. The spiral arms contain a large amount of gas and dust in the space between the stars, and they also contain the brightest stars in the galaxy. The third part is the halo, and it is not flattened like the disc. The Halo surrounds and extends through the disc.

Another type of galaxy is called elliptical. In this type the stars are arranged very smoothly, but there are more stars near the center than toward the edges. Most elliptical galaxies look like nothing more than fuzzy blobs of light. They are so far away that we do not see their individual stars but only the combined light of all their stars. Irregular

The great spiral nebula M31 in Andromeda is similar to our galaxy. The Andromeda nebula is twice the size of our galaxy and some nine hundred thousand parsecs away. The even sprinkling of stars in the foreground are in our galaxy, and the bright stars are as much as a thousand times brighter than our sun.

galaxies, a third type, have the greatest amount of interstellar gas and dust. Many bright new stars are formed from this material. Spirals have somewhat less gas and dust, and it is collected in their spiral arms. New stars form in the spiral arms and gradually spread throughout the rest of the disc, which consists of older stars. Elliptical galaxies have very little interstellar material and contain only old stars.

Galaxies contain from a million up to hundreds of billions of stars; the diameters, from 1,000 up to 50,000 parsecs (each parsec equals 3.26 light years). The Milky Way is larger than average but is not the largest galaxy that we know. Galaxies are spread

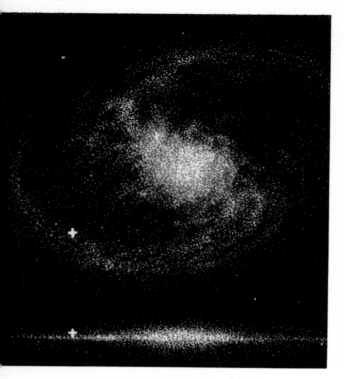

This is our galaxy, viewed from the side and top. The position of our solar system marked by the white cross.

Strong radio signals led astronomers to discover this pair of colliding galaxies in the constellation Cygnus.

Mt. Wilson & Palomar Observatories

through the universe about a million parsecs apart—some singly, others in groups. The Milky Way, for instance, has two companions, the irregular galaxies called the Magellanic Clouds. They are easily visible to the naked eye and look like two patches torn out of the Milky Way. They can be seen well only from the earth's Southern Hemisphere because they are so close to the South Celestial Pole.

Besides double and triple galaxies there are larger groups too. The Milky Way, for example, is part of a small cluster made up of a dozen and a half galaxies within the space of less than a million parsecs. Besides the Milky Way and the Magellanic Clouds there is one other triple system—the great spiral galaxy in Andromeda with its two elliptical companions. Also included in the group are one more spiral, two irregulars, and nine small elliptical galaxies. Other small galaxies could easily have escaped the notice of astronomers.

There are many other small groups of galaxies like the one to which the Milky Way belongs and also much larger clusters. The Virgo cluster, for example, includes many of the brightest galaxies in the sky. It has many hundreds of galaxies in a diameter of about a million parsecs. The Coma cluster, although more distant and therefore less conspicuous, has over 1,000 galaxies crowded into a diameter of a million parsecs. Other clusters are scattered through the universe in every direction. Not all galaxies are in clusters, though; many have no near neighbors.

All galaxies are in motion. Many rotate about their own axis, and the stars move back and forth. But each galaxy is also moving along as a whole—usually at a speed of 50 to 100 miles a second. Even so, the distances between galaxies are so large that most neighboring galaxies take a billion years to move past each other.

Besides these individual motions, the distant galaxies have a rapid motion in common. They all seem to be moving away from us, and the more distant ones appear to be moving faster than do those nearer our own galaxy. This is called the expansion of the universe.

In this barred spiral galaxy, the bars are composed of gas clouds that trail away from the galaxy's disk.

Globular galaxies, such as this, lack spiral arms. Their stars and interstellar gas and dust are compact.

An elliptical galaxy, with its many bright stars is more compact in the center than toward the outer edge.

A loose spiral galaxy, with trailing arms of gas and stars from the cluster forming the central disc.

As far as we can see into the distance, the universe is filled with galaxies. It is true that in some directions we see no galaxies, but this is only because the dust clouds of the Milky Way hinder our view. About a hundred million galaxies can be photographed with our largest telescopes, and with larger telescopes the number would be even larger. Since each of these galaxies contains many billions of stars, the number of stars in the observable part of the universe is truly tremendous. (See STARS; UNIVERSE.)

GALLINULES are fresh-water marsh birds found in warm-temperate and tropic zones throughout the world. Because they act and sound like chickens, in every language their common name includes "hen" or "chicken." In English, they are known as Mud, Moor, or Moat Hens or as Pond Chickens.

The Common Gallinule builds a nest of dried reeds lined with grass, wedged between growing weeds above the marsh water. The nest is edged with reeds broken off to form a bristly fence all around except for the entrance, a hole about three inches wide. The bird builds a reed walk, like a ship's gangway, from the entrance to the water below.

GALLS are abnormal plant growths produced by insects that lay their eggs in the tissue of the plant and develop inside the gall. Exactly what causes the gall is not known, but each species of insect always produces the same type of gall on a particular type of plant. If different species of gall-makers deposit eggs on the same type of plant, each forms its characteristic kind of gall. Members of five orders of insects—Diptera, Hymenop-

PURPLE GALLINULE—13 in.
Porphyrula martinica
Southern United States and West
Indies south to Uruguay and
northern Argentina

tera, Coleoptera, Lepidoptera, and Homoptera—form galls.

One of the most familiar galls is produced by the Goldenrod Gall Fly. Eggs deposited by the female in the unfolded leaves of a goldenrod's terminal bud hatch in one to two weeks, and the gall becomes large enough to be noticed about two weeks later. They reach full size—about an inch in diameter—in approximately a month. Inside the gall the maggot feeds and grows throughout the summer. When full grown, it prepares an exit tunnel to the outer wall, then moves back to the center of the gall where it remains all winter. In the spring the maggot pupates and emerges as an adult in about two weeks.

Oak apples are galls on the leaves and stems of oaks. They are produced by gall wasps (Cynipidae). Pine cone willow gall, another common type, is formed by a small gall midge (Itonididae).

Oak Apple Gall

Elliptical Goldenrod Gall

Goldenrod Gall

Blackberry Knot Gall

Galls or swellings on stems of golden rod, caused by fruit flies.

GARLIC (*Allium sativum*) is native to southeastern Europe where it has been used for over two thousand years. Garlic belongs to the same group of plants as onions (*Allium cepa*). It is used both fresh and dried as a flavoring for meats, soups, pickles, and salads. Garlic bulbs separate easily into segments called cloves or toes. In the United States, California, Texas, and Louisiana lead in garlic production. (See ONIONS.)

COMMON GALLINULE—14 in.
Gallinula chloropus
Temperate and tropical wetlands of the world, except Australia, New Zealand, and Papuan regions.

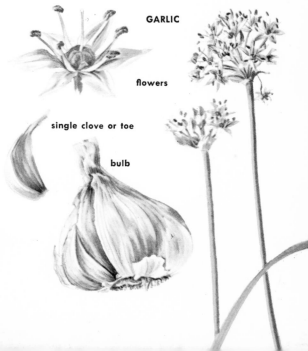

GARLIC

flowers

single clove or toe

bulb

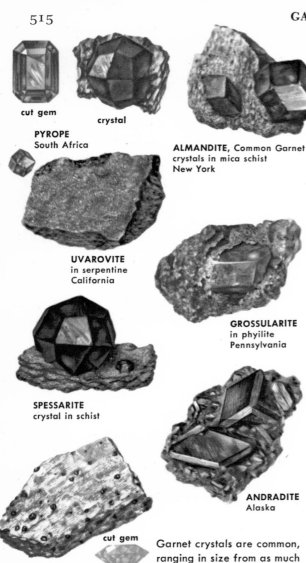

cut gem   crystal

PYROPE
South Africa

ALMANDITE, Common Garnet
crystals in mica schist
New York

UVAROVITE
in serpentine
California

GROSSULARITE
in phyilite
Pennsylvania

SPESSARITE
crystal in schist

ANDRADITE
Alaska

cut gem

ALMANDITE, Common Garnet
Pacific Northwest, U.S.

Garnet crystals are common, ranging in size from as much as 12 inches in diameter to no larger than a pinhead. Few are of gem quality.

GARNETS are a group of aluminum silicate minerals that have excellent crystal form. They have conchoidal fracture and a glassy luster. Most garnets are of metamorphic origin, their outstanding crystals develop by crowding aside the surrounding minerals. Garnets, which may vary greatly in color due to impurities, are usually grouped by chemical composition.

Almandite (an iron and aluminum garnet) is red-brown or dark red. It occurs in schists, gneisses, and sometimes in pegmatites. Some almandite crystals from the Adirondacks have grown over a foot in diameter.

Grossularite (a calcium and aluminum garnet) may be brown, yellow, or colorless. It is found in marble, schists, and nepheline-syenite. Pyrope (a magnesium and aluminum garnet) is deep red. It occurs in igneous rocks as rounded grains rather than crystals. Rhodolite (a magnesium, iron, and aluminum garnet) is a rose-red or purple found in schists. Spessartite (manganese and aluminum), a red or brown garnet, occurs in granites. Andradite (a calcium and iron garnet) is brown, yellow, or sometimes green. It occurs in syenite and also in such rocks as marble and schists. Uvarovite (calcium and chromium) is an emerald-green garnet that occurs in marble, gneisses, and serpentine. It is rarer than the other forms.

Transparent garnets may be used as gem stones. Darker ones are cut on cabochon and paler ones faceted (see GEMS). The principal use of garnet is as an abrasive and depends on its toughness, hardness, and the ability of the grains to break with sharp cutting edges. As garnet paper or cloth these abrasives are used for woodworking, leather and plastic finishing, and other grinding operations. Granular garnet is used for plate-glass and optical-lens grinding, metal polishing, and sand blasting. If garnet is roasted for several hours at 800-900 degrees centigrade, the toughness and sharpness of fracture of the gem stone is greatly increased.

Garnets are world-wide in occurrence in metamorphic areas. Commercial production in the United States is mainly in New York, Idaho, New Hampshire, and Florida (from sands). Excellent crystals have come from Switzerland, Czechoslovakia, Italy, Scandinavia, India, South Africa, Uruguay, Alaska, Quebec, Ontario, Connecticut, North Carolina, New Mexico, and California.

GARS (*Lepisosteus* spp.), primitive freshwater fishes, are living relics of a group of fishes common millions of years ago. The few species alive today inhabit warm, sluggish waters in the Mississippi basin and in Cuba and Central America. Long and slim, gars' bodies are covered with ganoid-type

LONGNOSE GAR
Lepisosteus osseus
Up to 5 ft.

SHORTNOSE GAR
Lepisosteus platostomus
Up to 2½ ft.

scales. These are so hard that Indians used them for arrowheads. Farmers once covered their plows with gar hides, which have also been used to make luggage. Gars often bask at the surface and can even live in stagnant water, their air bladders serving as lungs. Since they prey heavily on more desirable kinds of fish, they are destroyed wherever possible. Their flesh is seldom eaten, though it is palatable. Their eggs are poisonous.

Because of their sharp teeth, gars must be caught with a hook on a wire line, or they are caught in snares. Where the water is not clear, the fish are lured inside the loop with a bait. The wire pulls tight when they grab the bait and swim away with it. Many states allow the shooting or spearing of gars.

Gars are sometimes caught in wire snares. In some areas they are shot or speared.

GARTERSNAKES (*Thamnophis* spp.) of some 25 species range from southern Canada southward to mid-Central America. They occur even in cities where vacant lots, large yards, or parks provide refuge. They prefer open, grassy, or weeded areas. Where rainfall is scant, gartersnakes are usually found only along streams, lakes, and ponds.

All gartersnakes are basically the same in color pattern—one light stripe on each side and down the middle of the back and one or two rows of small dark spots between the stripes. In a few species the stripes are dim or even absent. A primitive species of central

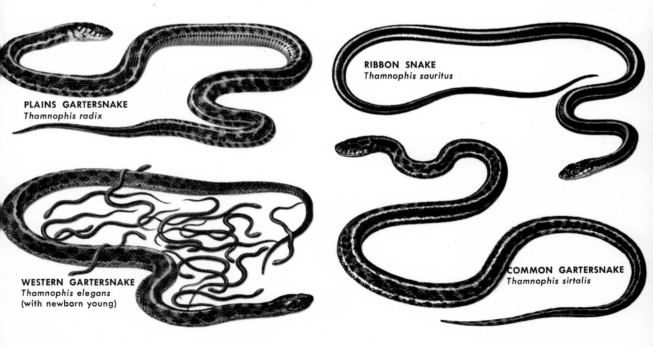

PLAINS GARTERSNAKE
Thamnophis radix

WESTERN GARTERSNAKE
Thamnophis elegans
(with newborn young)

RIBBON SNAKE
Thamnophis sauritus

COMMON GARTERSNAKE
Thamnophis sirtalis

Mexico has no stripes and is blotched like a water snake. At the other extreme is the slender, brightly striped Ribbon Snake in which the area between the stripes is black.

Gartersnakes range in size from about 20 to 48 inches. In some regions earthworms are their main diet. Frogs and small fish, either dead or alive, are eaten, and a few kinds feed on mice. Gartersnakes find their prey by its odor as well as its movement.

Gartersnakes give birth to their young—often as many as two or three dozen and rarely more than 70.

GASTROLITHS or Stomach Stones are round stones that were swallowed by large reptiles, apparently to assist in their digestion. They are generally found in the rib cage of the fossil. A fossil marine reptile found in rocks of Cretaceous age in South Dakota contained 253 stones (total weight, 18 pounds) in its abdominal region. (See FOSSILS.)

GAVIALS (*Gavialis gangeticus*) are crocodilians that live in the Indies, Ganges, and Brahmaputra rivers of India. Harmless to man except when attacked, the long-snouted Gavial feeds exclusively on fish and perhaps occasionally carrion. It is said to reach a length of 28 or 30 feet; the largest official record was 22 feet. (See CROCODILIANS.)

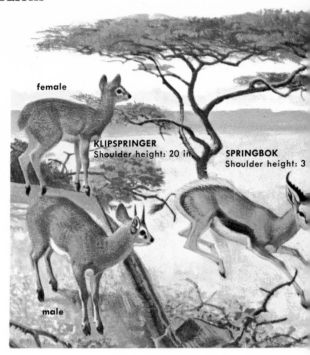

KLIPSPRINGER
Shoulder height: 20 in.

SPRINGBOK
Shoulder height: 3

female

male

GAVIAL
Gavialis gangeticus

GAZELLES, fleet-footed antelopes, live in open country where they can outrun most of their predators. Literature abounds with expressions which acknowledge the speed and gracefulness of these animals. Males have larger horns than females, and females of many kinds have no horns at all.

The Goitered Gazelle (*Gazella subgutturosa*), which lives in Persia northward to Central Asia, is so called because in the breeding season the male's neck swells to almost twice normal size. This swollen area resembles a goiter. The Goitered Gazelle is not very large, averaging only about 26 inches at its shoulders, but it runs very swiftly. Males have beautiful lyre-shaped horns. This antelope forages on grass and on the thick leaves of succulent desert plants.

Grant's Gazelle (*Gazella granti*), a large antelope of eastern Africa, may weigh as much as 150 pounds. Both sexes have long horns. Herds of these gazelles are common around water holes. Thomson's Gazelle (*Gazella thompsonii*), also found in Central Africa, is reddish in color but has distinctive black-and-white markings. Thomson's Gazelle has been a much-hunted game animal for many years in Kenya and Tanganyika.

Gerenuks (*Lithocranius walleri*), of eastern Africa, have large heads with exceedingly large horns on very long, thin necks. These animals stand on their hind legs to reach up into the trees for leaves.

Herds of many thousands of Springboks (*Antidorcas angolensis*), another gazelle-like animal, were once common in southern Africa. Like Impalas (*Aepyceros melanpus*), these animals are good jumpers. Impalas, which stand only about three feet tall at their shoulders, can leap eight feet high and seem to enjoy jumping over one another. In horizontal jumps they can span 35 feet.

Klipspringers (*Oreotragus oreotragus*), small gazelle-like mammals of tropical African mountains, measure only about 20 inches high at the shoulder. Like the Mountain Goats of North America and the Chamois of the Alps, these gazelles are adept at springing up and down steep rocky slopes.

GECKOS, the most primitive of living lizards, are small to medium-sized and worldwide in distribution. In many tropical regions geckos are the most abundant lizards. Most species are active only at dusk or at night. A few kinds are common around dwellings where they congregate on walls and ceilings and especially around lights to catch insects.

All geckos—some 450 species of three families—have very tender, easily torn skin. They lack bony scales. Tails of all except two species of southwestern Asia are delicate and easily broken off. A new tail grows back quickly, however. A partial break often results in a branched tail. The largest species measure 14 inches in length; the shortest is a dwarf gecko (*Sphaerodactylus elegans*), only 1½ inches long—the smallest known reptile.

Dwarf geckos live in the West Indies and in Central and South America. This is the only group of geckos without a voice. Some have a single, round pad at the tip of each finger and toe; others have no pads. Unlike other geckos, the pupil of the eye in dwarf geckos is round, elliptical, or vertical, rather than lobed and vertical. They are active in daylight but not in bright sun. No dwarf geckos occur natively in the United States, but two species introduced from the West Indies are established in southern Florida.

Eyelidded geckos are the most primitive of the geckos. Ground geckos (*Coleonyx*), which live in southwestern United States and southward through Central America, are the only members of this group in the Western Hemisphere. All others are in Africa and southern Asia. All have eyelids much like most other lizards and slender fingers and toes without

Gazelles are extremely graceful when running. They seem to soar through air between powerful leaps.

GRANT'S GAZELLE
shoulder height: 33 in.

GERENUK
shoulder height: 41 in.

TOKAY GECKO
Gekko gekko

MADAGASCAR GECKO
Phelsuma madagascariensis

pads. None of the other geckos have movable eyelids, and most others have pads on their hands and feet. Eyelidded geckos usually lay two eggs, as do most other geckos, and they utter long, drawn-out rattles quite unlike the single croaks uttered by other geckos.

Both ground and dwarf geckos have long, slender, round tails. In some kinds the tail is swollen at the base so that it is carrot-shaped. In one a knob occurs at the tip of the tail. Many have flattened tails, sometimes fringed with projecting scales on each side. Others have thin, fleshy lobes or broad, leaflike expansions which help in gliding flights from high trees. Geckos that are gliders also have fringes along the sides of the body.

Some 400 species belong to the family of "true" geckos. The large lower eyelid is fused with the small upper one and has in the center a transparent scale, called a "spectacle" or "brille," through which the lizard can see. Snakes have the same sort of spectacle, and this is one of the similarities suggesting that snakes arose from gecko-like ancestors.

True geckos have distinct voices. Geckos are, in fact, the only lizards that really have voices. The sound produced is a single croak, though sometimes of two distinct parts. The very name gecko is an attempt to convey by word the sound made by the common House Gecko (*Hemidactylus mabouia*) of North Africa. The Tokay, largest of the geckos, gives a loud cry. In the sand dunes of southwestern Africa the abundant Garrulous Geckos (*Ptenopus garrulus*) emerge in early evening and create a din like a frog chorus.

Most true geckos are active in late afternoon and after dark. Their eyes are so sensitive to light that they can see in nearly total darkness. The pupil is slitlike instead of round, and the edges of the slit are lobed so that three of four pinhole-sized openings remain along the vertical line when the slit is closed. This gives a sharp focus on objects both near and far. Geckos of Madagascar differ in being active during the day.

Most true geckos have a fairly large pad on each finger and toe. These pads are responsible for the extraordinary ability of geckos to walk on ceilings, walls, and other smooth surfaces. Though seemingly smooth, the pads are coated with many thousands of tiny hooks that catch on tiny irregularities.

True geckos lay eggs, typically two. These are stuck to tree bark, window shutters, or in other hidden spots. The eggs are more or less round, white, and hardshelled. A few New Zealand geckos give birth to their young.

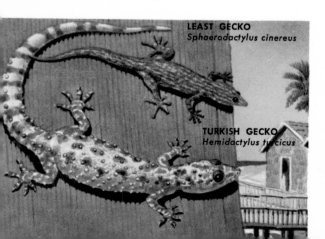

LEAST GECKO
Sphaerodactylus cinereus

TURKISH GECKO
Hemidactylus turcicus

THE NEXT BOOK IN THIS SERIES

GEESE TO HERRINGS

CONTRIBUTING ARTISTS

Dorothea & Sy Barlowe
Walter Ferguson
Hans Helweg
Matthew Kalmenoff
Bob Kuhn
Jack Kunz
Rene Martin
Harry McNaught
Fred Poffenberger
Marita & George Sandström
Alex Seidel
Arthur Singer
Elmer Smith
Ann Ophelia Todd
Dan Todd
Barbara Wolff
Rudy Zallinger
Photographers and other sources
are credited under the picture.